Cautionary Tales
and other verses

Cautionary Tales
and other verses by
Hilaire Belloc

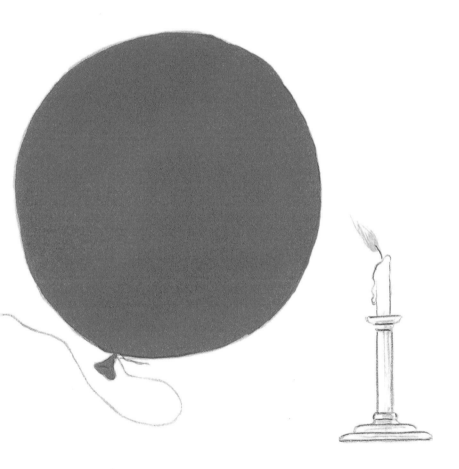

Illustrated by Posy Simmonds

LONDON
THE FOLIO SOCIETY 1997

This collection was first published in 1939
by Gerald Duckworth & Co. Ltd under the title
Cautionary Verses: The Collected Humorous Poems

Reprinted by permission of Jonathan Cape Ltd

This edition published by The Folio Society Ltd,
44 Eagle Street, London WC1R 4FS
www.foliosociety.com

Seventh printing 2012

Typeset in Walbaum at The Folio Society.
Printed on Abbey Pure paper at Martins the
Printers Ltd, Berwick-upon-Tweed. Bound by
Hunter & Foulis, Edinburgh, in cloth printed
and blocked with a design by the artist

Contents

MORE PEERS (1911) 81

A MORAL ALPHABET (1899) 91

LADIES AND GENTLEMEN (1932) 107

THE MODERN TRAVELLER (1898) 121

Colour Illustrations

Child! do not throw this book about;
  Refrain from the unholy pleasure
Of cutting all the pictures out!
  Preserve it as your chiefest treasure.

Child, have you never heard it said
  That you are heir to all the ages?
Why, then, your hands were never made
  To tear these beautiful thick pages!

Your little hands were made to take
  The better things and leave the worse ones.
They also may be used to shake
  The Massive Paws of Elder Persons.

And when your prayers complete the day,
  Darling, your little tiny hands
Were also made, I think, to pray
  For men that lose their fairylands.

CAUTIONARY TALES FOR CHILDREN

INTRODUCTION

Upon being asked by a Reader whether the verses contained in this book were true.

And is it True? It is not True.
And if it were it wouldn't do,
For people such as me and you
Who pretty nearly all day long
Are doing something rather wrong.
Because if things were really so,
You would have perished long ago,
And I would not have lived to write
The noble lines that meet your sight,
Nor POSY SIMMONDS *come to draw*
The nicest things you ever saw.

H. B.

JIM

Who ran away from his Nurse,
and was eaten by a Lion

There was a Boy whose name was Jim;
His Friends were very good to him.
They gave him Tea, and Cakes, and Jam,
And slices of delicious Ham,
And Chocolate with pink inside,
And little Tricycles to ride,
And read him Stories through and through,
And even took him to the Zoo—
But there it was the dreadful Fate
Befel him, which I now relate.

You know—at least you *ought* to know,
For I have often told you so—
That Children never are allowed
To leave their Nurses in a Crowd;
Now this was Jim's especial Foible,
He ran away when he was able,
And on this inauspicious day
He slipped his hand and ran away!
He hadn't gone a yard when—Bang!
With open Jaws, a Lion sprang,
And hungrily began to eat
The Boy: beginning at his feet.

Now, just imagine how it feels
When first your toes and then your heels,
And then by gradual degrees,
Your shins and ankles, calves and knees,
Are slowly eaten, bit by bit.
No wonder Jim detested it!
No wonder that he shouted 'Hi!'
The Honest Keeper heard his cry,

Though very fat he almost ran
To help the little gentleman.
'Ponto!' he ordered as he came
(For Ponto was the Lion's name),
'Ponto!' he cried, with angry Frown.
'Let go, Sir! Down, Sir! Put it down!'

The Lion made a sudden Stop,
He let the Dainty Morsel drop,
And slunk reluctant to his Cage,
Snarling with Disappointed Rage.
But when he bent him over Jim,
The Honest Keeper's Eyes were dim.
The Lion having reached his Head,
The Miserable Boy was dead!
When Nurse informed his Parents, they
Were more Concerned than I can say:
His Mother, as she dried her eyes,
Said, 'Well—it gives me no surprise,
He would not do as he was told!'
His Father, who was self-controlled,
Bade all the children round attend
To James's miserable end,
And always keep a-hold of Nurse
For fear of finding something worse.

HENRY KING

Who chewed bits of String, and was early
cut off in Dreadful Agonies

The Chief Defect of Henry King
   Was chewing little bits of String.
At last he swallowed some which tied
   Itself in ugly Knots inside.
Physicians of the Utmost Fame
Were called at once; but when they came
They answered, as they took their Fees,
'There is no Cure for this Disease.
Henry will very soon be dead.'
His Parents stood about his Bed
Lamenting his Untimely Death,
When Henry, with his Latest Breath,
Cried—'Oh, my Friends, be warned by me,
That Breakfast, Dinner, Lunch, and Tea
Are all the Human Frame requires . . .'
With that, the Wretched Child expires.

MATILDA

Who told Lies,
and was Burned to Death

Matilda told such Dreadful Lies,
It made one Gasp and Stretch one's Eyes;
Her Aunt, who, from her Earliest Youth,
Had kept a Strict Regard for Truth,
Attempted to Believe Matilda:
The effort very nearly killed her,
And would have done so, had not She
Discovered this Infirmity.
For once, towards the Close of Day,
Matilda, growing tired of play,
And finding she was left alone,
Went tiptoe to the Telephone
And summoned the Immediate Aid
Of London's Noble Fire-Brigade.
Within an hour the Gallant Band
Were pouring in on every hand,
From Putney, Hackney Downs, and Bow
With Courage high and Hearts a-glow
They galloped, roaring through the Town,
'Matilda's House is Burning Down!'
Inspired by British Cheers and Loud
Proceeding from the Frenzied Crowd,
They ran their ladders through a score
Of windows on the Ballroom Floor;
And took Peculiar Pains to Souse
The Pictures up and down the House,
Until Matilda's Aunt succeeded
In showing them they were not needed
And even then she had to pay
To get the Men to go away!

*

It happened that a few Weeks later
Her Aunt was off to the Theatre
To see that Interesting Play
The Second Mrs Tanqueray.
She had refused to take her Niece
To hear this Entertaining Piece:
A Deprivation Just and Wise
To Punish her for Telling Lies.
That Night a Fire *did* break out—
You should have heard Matilda Shout!
You should have heard her Scream and Bawl,
And throw the window up and call
To People passing in the Street—
(The rapidly increasing Heat
Encouraging her to obtain
Their confidence)—but all in vain!
For every time She shouted 'Fire!'
They only answered 'Little Liar!'
And therefore when her Aunt returned,
Matilda, and the House, were Burned.

FRANKLIN HYDE

Who caroused in the Dirt
and was corrected by His Uncle

His Uncle came on Franklin Hyde
Carousing in the Dirt.
He Shook him hard from Side to Side
And Hit him till it Hurt,
Exclaiming, with a Final Thud,
'Take that! Abandoned Boy!
For Playing with Disgusting Mud
As though it were a Toy!'

MORAL

From Franklin Hyde's adventure, learn
To pass your Leisure Time
In Cleanly Merriment, and turn
From Mud and Ooze and Slime
And every form of Nastiness—
But, on the other Hand,
Children in ordinary Dress
May always play with Sand.

GODOLPHIN HORNE

Who was cursed with the Sin of Pride,
and Became a Boot-Black

Godolphin Horne was Nobly Born;
He held the Human Race in Scorn,
And lived with all his Sisters where
His Father lived, in Berkeley Square.
And oh! the Lad was Deathly Proud!
He never shook your Hand or Bowed,
But merely smirked and nodded thus:
How perfectly ridiculous!
Alas! That such Affected Tricks
Should flourish in a Child of Six!
(For such was Young Godolphin's age.)
Just then, the Court required a Page,
Whereat the Lord High Chamberlain
(The Kindest and the Best of Men),
He went good-naturedly and took
A Perfectly Enormous Book
Called *People Qualified to Be*
Attendant on His Majesty,
And murmured, as he scanned the list
(To see that no one should be missed),
'There's William Coutts has got the Flu,
And Billy Higgs would never do,
And Guy de Vere is far too young,
And . . . wasn't D'Alton's Father hung?
And as for Alexander Byng!. . .
I think I know the kind of thing,
A Churchman, cleanly, nobly born,
Come let us say Godolphin Horne?'
But hardly had he said the word
When Murmurs of Dissent were heard.
The King of Iceland's Eldest Son
Said, 'Thank you! I am taking none!'

The Aged Duchess of Athlone
Remarked, in her sub-acid tone,
'I doubt if He is what we need!'
With which the Bishops all agreed;
And even Lady Mary Flood
(*So* Kind, and oh! so *really* good)
Said, 'No! He wouldn't do at all,
He'd make us feel a lot too small.'
The Chamberlain said, '. . . Well, well, well!
No doubt you're right . . . One cannot tell!'
He took his Gold and Diamond Pen
And Scratched Godolphin out again.
So now Godolphin is the Boy
Who blacks the Boots at the Savoy.

ALGERNON

*Who played with a Loaded Gun,
and, on missing his Sister,
was reprimanded by his Father*

Young Algernon, the Doctor's Son,
Was playing with a Loaded Gun.
He pointed it towards his sister,
Aimed very carefully, but Missed her!
His Father, who was standing near,
The Loud Explosion chanced to Hear,
And reprimanded Algernon
For playing with a Loaded Gun.

HILDEBRAND

Who was frightened by a Passing Motor,
and was brought to Reason

'Oh Murder! What was that, Papa!'
'My child, it was a Motor Car,
A Most Ingenious Toy!
Designed to Captivate and Charm
Much rather than to rouse Alarm
In any English Boy.

'What would your Great Grandfather who
Was Aide-de-Camp to General Brue,
And lost a leg at Waterloo,
And Quatre-Bras and Ligny too!
And died at Trafalgar!
What would he have remarked to hear
His Young Descendant shriek with fear,
Because he happened to be near
    A Harmless Motor Car!
But do not fret about it! Come!
We'll off to Town and purchase some!'

LORD LUNDY

Who was too Freely Moved to Tears,
and thereby ruined his Political Career

Lord Lundy from his earliest years
Was far too freely moved to Tears.
For instance, if his Mother said,
'Lundy! It's time to go to Bed!'
He bellowed like a Little Turk.
Or if his father, Lord Dunquerque
Said, 'Hi!' in a Commanding Tone,
'Hi, Lundy! Leave the Cat alone!'
Lord Lundy, letting go its tail,
Would raise so terrible a wail
As moved his Grandpapa the Duke
To utter the severe rebuke:
'When I, Sir! was a little Boy,
An Animal was not a Toy!'

His father's Elder Sister, who
Was married to a Parvenoo,
Confided to Her Husband, 'Drat!
The Miserable, Peevish Brat!
Why don't they drown the Little Beast!'
Suggestions which, to say the least,
Are not what we expect to hear
From Daughters of an English Peer.
His grandmamma, His Mother's Mother,
Who had some dignity or other,
The Garter, or no matter what,
I can't remember all the Lot!
Said, 'Oh! that I were Brisk and Spry
To give him that for which to cry!'
(An empty wish, alas! for she
Was Blind and nearly ninety-three.)

The Dear old Butler thought—but there!
I really neither know nor care
For what the Dear Old Butler thought!
In my opinion, Butlers ought
To know their place, and not to play
The Old Retainer night and day.
I'm getting tired and so are you,
Let's cut the Poem into two!

LORD LUNDY

It happened to Lord Lundy then,
As happens to so many men:
Towards the age of twenty-six,
They shoved him into politics;
In which profession he commanded
The income that his rank demanded
In turn as Secretary for
India, the Colonies, and War.
But very soon his friends began
To doubt if he were quite the man:
Thus, if a member rose to say
(As members do from day to day),
'Arising out of that reply . . . !'
Lord Lundy would begin to cry.
A Hint at harmless little jobs
Would shake him with convulsive sobs.

While as for Revelations, these
Would simply bring him to his knees,
And leave him whimpering like a child.
It drove his Colleagues raving wild!
They let him sink from Post to Post,
From fifteen hundred at the most
To eight, and barely six—and then
To be Curator of Big Ben! . . .
And finally there came a Threat
To oust him from the Cabinet!

The Duke—his aged grand-sire—bore
The shame till he could bear no more.
He rallied his declining powers,
Summoned the youth to Brackley Towers,
And bitterly addressed him thus—
'Sir! you have disappointed us!

We had intended you to be
The next Prime Minister but three:
The stocks were sold; the Press was squared;
The Middle Class was quite prepared.
But as it is! . . . My language fails!
Go out and govern New South Wales!'

*

The Aged Patriot groaned and died:
And gracious! how Lord Lundy cried!

REBECCA

Who slammed Doors for Fun and Perished Miserably

A trick that everyone abhors
In Little Girls is slamming Doors.
A Wealthy Banker's Little Daughter
Who lived in Palace Green, Bayswater
(By name Rebecca Offendort),
Was given to this Furious Sport.

She would deliberately go
And Slam the door like Billy-Ho!
To make her Uncle Jacob start.
She was not really bad at heart,
But only rather rude and wild:
She was an aggravating child . . .

It happened that a Marble Bust
Of Abraham was standing just
Above the Door this little Lamb
Had carefully prepared to Slam,
And Down it came! It knocked her flat!
It laid her out! She looked like that.

*

Her funeral Sermon (which was long
And followed by a Sacred Song)
Mentioned her Virtues, it is true,
But dwelt upon her Vices too,
And showed the Dreadful End of One
Who goes and slams the door for Fun.

*

The children who were brought to hear
The awful Tale from far and near
Were much impressed, and inly swore
They never more would slam the Door.
—As often they had done before.

GEORGE

Who played with a Dangerous Toy,
and suffered a Catastrophe of
considerable Dimensions

When George's Grandmamma was told
That George had been as good as Gold,
She Promised in the Afternoon
To buy him an *Immense BALLOON.*
And so she did; but when it came,
It got into the candle flame,
And being of a dangerous sort
Exploded with a loud report!

The Lights went out! The Windows broke!
The Room was filled with reeking smoke.
And in the darkness shrieks and yells
Were mingled with Electric Bells,
And falling masonry and groans,
And crunching, as of broken bones,
And dreadful shrieks, when, worst of all,
The House itself began to fall!
It tottered, shuddering to and fro,
Then crashed into the street below—
Which happened to be Savile Row.

*

When Help arrived, among the Dead
Were Cousin Mary, Little Fred,
The Footmen (both of them), The Groom,
The man that cleaned the Billiard-Room,
The Chaplain, and the Still-Room Maid.
And I am dreadfully afraid
That Monsieur Champignon, the Chef,
Will now be permanently deaf—

And both his Aides are much the same;
While George, who was in part to blame,
Received, you will regret to hear,
A nasty lump behind the ear.

MORAL

The moral is that little Boys
Should not be given dangerous Toys.

CHARLES AUGUSTUS FORTESCUE

Who always Did what was Right, and so accumulated an Immense Fortune

The nicest child I ever knew
Was Charles Augustus Fortescue.
He never lost his cap, or tore
His stockings or his pinafore:
    In eating Bread he made no Crumbs,
    He was extremely fond of sums,
To which, however, he preferred
The Parsing of a Latin Word—
He sought, when it was in his power,
For information twice an hour,
And as for finding Mutton-Fat
Unappetising, far from that!
He often, at his Father's Board,
Would beg them, of his own accord,
To give him, if they did not mind,
The Greasiest Morsels they could find—
His Later Years did not belie
The Promise of his Infancy.
In Public Life he always tried
To take a judgement Broad and Wide;
In Private, none was more than he
Renowned for quiet courtesy.
He rose at once in his Career,
And long before his Fortieth Year
Had wedded Fifi, Only Child
Of Bunyan, First Lord Aberfylde.
He thus became immensely Rich,
And built the Splendid Mansion which
Is called '*The Cedars, Muswell Hill*',
Where he resides in Affluence still
To show what Everybody might
Become by SIMPLY DOING RIGHT.

NEW CAUTIONARY TALES

A REPROOF OF GLUTTONY

The Elephant will eat of hay
Some four and twenty tons a day,
And in his little eyes express
His unaffected thankfulness
That Providence should deign to find
Him food of this delicious kind.
While they that pay for all the hay
Will frequently be heard to say
How highly privileged they feel
To help him make so large a meal.
The Boa Constrictor dotes on goats;
The Horse is quite content with oats,
Or will alternatively pass
A happy morning munching grass.
The great Ant Eater of Taluz
Consumes—or people say he does—
Not only what his name implies
But even ordinary flies:
And Marmosets and Chimpanzees
Are happy on the nuts of trees.
The Lion from the burning slopes
Of Atlas lives on Antelopes,
And only adds the flesh of men
By way of relish now and then;
As Cheetahs—yes, and Tigers, too,
And Jaguars of the Andes—do.
The Lobster, I have heard it said,
Eats nobody till he is dead;
And Cobras, though they have the sense
To poison you in self-defence,
Restrict their food to birds and hares:
Which also may be true of Bears.
Indeed wherever we survey
Our Humble Friends we find that they
Confine their appetites to what
May happen to be on the spot.

Simplicity and moderation
Distinguish all the Brute Creation.
But Man—proud man! (as Dryden sings)
Though wolfing quantities of things—
Smoked Salmon in transparent slices,
And Turbot à la Reine, and Ices,
And Truffled Pies and Caviare,
And Chinese Ginger from the Jar;
And Oysters; and a kind of stuff
Called Cassouletto (good enough!)
And Mutton duly steeped in claret
(Or jumped with young shallot and carrot),
And Chicken Livers done with rice,
And Quails (which, I am told, are Mice),
And Peaches from a sunny wall,
And—Lord! I don't know what and all!—
Oh! Yes! And Sausages—is not
Contented with his Prandial lot.

MORAL

The Moral is (I think, at least)
That Man is an UNGRATEFUL BEAST.

MARIA

Who made Faces
and a Deplorable Marriage

Maria loved to pull a face:
And no such commonplace grimace
As you or I or anyone
Might make at grandmamma for fun.
But one where nose and mouth and all
Were screwed into a kind of ball,
The which—as you may well expect—
Produced a horrible effect
On those it was directed at.
One morning she was struck like that!—
Her features took their final mould
In shapes that made your blood run cold
And wholly lost their former charm.
Mamma, in agonised alarm,
Consulted a renowned Masseuse
—An old and valued friend of hers—
Who rubbed the wretched child for days
In five and twenty different ways
And after that began again.
But all in vain!—But all in vain!
The years advance: Maria grows
Into a Blooming English Rose—
With every talent, every grace
(Save in this trifle of the face).
She sang, recited, laughed and played
At all that an accomplished maid
Should play with skill to be of note—
Golf, the Piano, and the Goat;
She talked in French till all was blue
And knew a little German too.
She told the tales that soldiers tell,
She also danced extremely well,

Her wit was pointed, loud and raw,
She shone at laying down the law,
She drank liqueurs instead of tea,
Her verse was admirably free
And quoted in the latest books—
But people couldn't stand her looks.
Her parents had with thoughtful care
Proclaimed her genius everywhere,
Nor quite concealed a wealth which sounds
Enormous—thirty million pounds—
And further whispered it that she
Could deal with it exclusively.
They did not hide her chief defect,
But what with birth and intellect
And breeding and such ample means,
And still in her delightful 'teens,
A girl like our Maria (they thought)
Should make the kind of match she ought.
Those who had seen her here at home
Might hesitate: but Paris? Rome? . . .
—The foreigners should take the bait.
And so they did. At any rate,
The greatest men of every land
Arrived in shoals to seek her hand,
Grand Dukes, Commanders of the Fleece,
Mysterious Millionaires from Greece,
And exiled Kings in large amounts,
Ambassadors and Papal Counts,
And Rastaquouères from Palamerez
And Famous Foreign Secretaries,
They came along in turns to call
But *all*—without exception, *all*—
Though with determination set,
Yet, when they actually *met*,
Would start convulsively as though
They had received a sudden blow,
And mumbling a discreet good-day
Would shuffle, turn and slink away.

The upshot of it was Maria
Was married to a neighbouring Squire
Who, being blind, could never guess
His wife's appalling ugliness.
The man was independent, dull,
Offensive, poor and masterful.
It was a very dreadful thing! . . .
Now let us turn to Sarah Byng.

SARAH BYNG

Who could not read and was tossed
into a thorny hedge by a Bull

Some years ago you heard me sing
My doubts on Alexander Byng.
His sister Sarah now inspires
My jaded Muse, my failing fires.
Of Sarah Byng the tale is told
How when the child was twelve years old
She could not read or write a line.
Her sister Jane, though barely nine,
Could spout the Catechism through
And parts of Matthew Arnold too,
While little Bill who came between
Was quite unnaturally keen
On 'Athalie', by Jean Racine.
But not so Sarah! Not so Sal!
She was a most uncultured girl
Who didn't care a pinch of snuff
For any literary stuff
And gave the classics all a miss.
Observe the consequence of this!
As she was walking home one day
Upon the fields across her way
A gate, securely padlocked, stood,
And by its side a piece of wood
On which was painted plain and full,

BEWARE THE VERY FURIOUS BULL

Alas! The young illiterate
Went blindly forward to her fate,
And ignorantly climbed the gate!
Now happily the Bull that day
Was rather in the mood for play

Than goring people through and through
As Bulls so very often do;
He tossed her lightly with his horns
Into a prickly hedge of thorns,
And stood by laughing while she strode
And pushed and struggled to the road.
The lesson was not lost upon
The child, who since has always gone
A long way round to keep away
From signs, whatever they may say,
And leaves a padlocked gate alone.
Moreover she has wisely grown
Confirmed in her instinctive guess
That literature breeds distress.

JACK AND HIS PONY, TOM

Jack had a little pony—Tom;
He frequently would take it from
The stable where it used to stand
And give it sugar with his hand.
He also gave it oats and hay
And carrots twenty times a day
And grass in basketfuls, and greens,
And Swedes and mangolds also beans
And patent foods from various sources
And bread (which isn't good for horses)
And chocolate and apple-rings
And lots and lots of other things
The most of which do not agree
With Polo Ponies such as he.
And all in such a quantity
As ruined his digestion wholly
And turned him from a Ponopoly
—I mean a Polo Pony—into
A case that clearly must be seen to.
Because he swelled and swelled and swelled.
Which, when the kindly boy beheld,
He gave him medicine by the pail
And malted milk, and nutmeg ale,
And yet it only swelled the more
Until its stomach touched the floor,
And then it heaved and groaned as well
And staggered, till at last it fell
And found it could not rise again.
Jack wept and prayed—but all in vain.
The pony died, and as it died
Kicked him severely in the side.

MORAL

Kindness to animals should be
Attuned to their brutality.

TOM AND HIS PONY, JACK

Tom had a little pony, Jack:
He vaulted lightly on its back
And galloped off for miles and miles,
A-leaping hedges, gates and stiles,
And shouting 'Yoicks!' and 'Tally-Ho!'
And 'Heads I win!' and 'Tails below!'
And many another sporting phrase.
He rode like this for several days,
Until the pony, feeling tired,
Collapsed, looked heavenward and expired.
His father made a fearful row.
He said 'By Gum, you've done it now!
Here lies—a carcase on the ground—
No less than five-and-twenty pound!
Indeed the value of the beast
Would probably have much increased.
His teeth were false; and all were told
That he was only four years old.
Oh! Curse it all! I tell you plain
I'll never let you ride again.'

MORAL

His father died when he was twenty
And left three horses, which is plenty.

ABOUT JOHN

Who lost a Fortune by Throwing Stones

JOHN VAVASSOUR DE QUENTIN JONES
Was very fond of throwing stones
At Horses, People, Passing Trains,
But 'specially at Window-panes.
Like many of the Upper Class
He liked the Sound of Broken Glass*
It bucked him up and made him gay:
It was his favourite form of Play.
But the Amusement cost him dear,
My children, as you now shall hear.

JOHN VAVASSOUR DE QUENTIN had
An uncle, who adored the lad:
And often chuckled; 'Wait until
You see what's left you in my will!'
Nor were the words without import,
Because this uncle did a sort
Of something in the City, which
Had made him fabulously rich.
(Although his brother, John's papa,
Was poor, as many fathers are.)
He had a lot of stocks and shares
And half a street in Buenos Aires†
A bank in Rio, and a line
Of Steamers to the Argentine.
And options more than I can tell,
And bits of Canada as well;

* A line I stole with subtle daring
  From Wing-Commander Maurice Baring.
† But this pronunciation varies
  Some people call it Bu-enos Airés.

He even had a mortgage on
The House inhabited by John.
His will, the cause of all the fuss,
Was carefully indited thus:

   'This is the last and solemn Will
Of Uncle William—known as Bill.
I do bequeath, devise and give
By Execution Mandative
The whole amount of what I've got
(It comes to a tremendous lot!)
In seizin to devolve upon
My well-beloved nephew John.
(And here the witnesses will sign
Their names upon the dotted line.)'

   Such was the Legal Instrument
Expressing Uncle Bill's intent.

   As time went on declining Health
Transmogrified this Man of Wealth;
And it was excellently clear
That Uncle Bill's demise was near.

At last his sole idea of fun
Was sitting snoozling in the sun.
So once, when he would take the air,
They wheeled him in his Patent Chair
(By 'They', I mean his Nurse, who came
From Dorchester upon the Thame:
Miss Charming was the Nurse's name)
To where beside a little wood
A long abandoned greenhouse stood,
And there he sank into a doze
Of senile and inept repose.
But not for long his drowsy ease!
A stone came whizzing through the trees,
And caught him smartly in the eye.
He woke with an appalling cry,

And shrieked in agonising tones:
'Oh! Lord! Whoever's throwing stones!'
Miss Charming, who was standing near,
Said: 'That was Master John, I fear!'
'Go, get my Ink-pot and my Quill,
My Blotter and my Famous Will.'
Miss Charming flew as though on wings
To fetch these necessary things,
And Uncle William ran his pen
Through 'well-beloved John', and then
Proceeded, in the place of same,
To substitute Miss Charming's name:
Who now resides in Portman Square
And is accepted everywhere.

PETER GOOLE

Who Ruined his Father and Mother by Extravagance

PART I

Young Peter Goole, a child of nine,
Gave little reason to complain.
Though an imaginative youth
He very often told the truth,
And never tried to black the eyes
Of Comrades of superior size.
He did his lessons (more or less)
Without extravagant distress,
And showed sufficient intellect,
But failed in one severe defect;
It seems he wholly lacked a sense
Of limiting the day's expense,
And money ran between his hands
Like water through the Ocean Sands.
Such conduct could not but affect
His parent's fortune, which was wrecked
Like many and many another one
By folly in a spendthrift son:
By that most tragical mischance,
An Only Child's Extravagance.

There came a day when Mr Goole
—The Father of this little fool—
With nothing in the bank at all
Was up against it, like a wall.
He wrang his hands, exclaiming, 'If
I only had a bit of Stiff
How different would be my life!'
Whereat his true and noble wife
Replied, to comfort him, 'Alas!
I said that this would come to pass!

Nothing can keep us off the rocks
But Peter's little Money Box.'
The Father, therefore (and his wife),
They prised it open with a knife—
But nothing could be found therein
Save two bone buttons and a pin.

PART II

They had to sell the house and grounds
For less than twenty thousand pounds,
And so retired, with broken hearts,
To vegetate in foreign parts,
And ended their declining years
At Blidah—which is near Algiers.
There, in the course of time, they died,
And there lie buried side by side.
While when we turn to Peter, he
The cause of this catastrophe,
There fell upon him such a fate
As makes me shudder to relate.
Just in its fifth and final year,
His University Career
Was blasted by the new and dread
Necessity of earning bread.
He was compelled to join a firm
Of Brokers—in the summer term!

And even now, at twenty-five,
He has to WORK to keep alive!
Yes! All day long from 10 till 4!
For half the year or even more;
With but an hour or two to spend
At luncheon with a city friend.

AUNT JANE

'Mamma,' said AMANDA, 'I want to know what
   Our relatives mean when they say
That Aunt Jane is a Gorgon who ought to be shot,
   Or at any rate taken away.

'Pray what is a Gorgon and why do you shoot
   It? Or are its advances refused?
Or is it perhaps a maleficent Brute?
   I protest I am wholly bemused.'

'The Term', said her Mother, 'is certain to pain,
   And is quite inexcusably rude.
Moreover Aunt Jane, though uncommonly plain,
   Is also uncommonly good.

'She provides information without hesitation,
   For people unwilling to learn;
And often bestows good advice upon those
   Who give her no thanks in return.

'She is down before anyone's up in the place—
   That is, up before anyone's down.
Her Domestics are awed by the shape of her face
   And they tremble with fear at her frown.

'Her visiting list is of Clergymen who
   Have reached a respectable age,
And she pays her companion MISS ANGELA DREW
   A sufficient and regular wage.

'Her fortune is large, though we often remark
   On a modesty rare in the rich;
For her nearest and dearest are quite in the dark
   As to what she will leave, or to which.

'Her conduct has ever been totally free
    From censorious whispers of ill,
At any rate, since 1903—
    And probably earlier still.

'Your Father's dear sister presents in a word,
    A model for all of her sex,
With a firmness of will that is never deterred,
    And a confidence nothing can vex.

'I can only desire that you too should aspire
    To such earthly reward as appears
In a high reputation, at present entire,
    After Heaven knows how many years.

'So in future remember to turn a deaf ear
    To detraction—and now run away
To your brothers and sisters whose laughter I hear
    In the garden below us at play.'

'Oh, thank you, Mamma!' said AMANDA at that,
    And ran off to the innocent band
Who were merrily burying Thomas the Cat
    Right up to his neck in the sand.

ON FOOD

Alas! What various tastes in food,
Divide the human brotherhood!
Birds in their little nests agree
With Chinamen, but not with me.
Colonials like their oysters hot,
Their Omelettes heavy—I do not.
The French are fond of slugs and frogs,
The Siamese eat puppy dogs.
The nobles at the brilliant Court
Of Muscovy consumed a sort
Of candles held and eaten thus,
As though they were asparagus.
The Spaniard, I have heard it said,
Eats garlic, by itself, on bread:
Now just suppose a friend or dun
Dropped in to lunch at half-past one
And you were jovially to say,
'Here's bread and garlic! Peg away!'
I doubt if you would gain your end
Or soothe the dun, or please the friend.

In Italy the traveller notes
With great disgust the flesh of goats
Appearing on the table d'hôtes;
And even this the natives spoil
By frying it in rancid oil.
In Maryland they charge like sin
For nasty stuff called terrapin;
And when they ask you out to dine
At Washington, instead of wine,
They give you water from the spring
With lumps of ice for flavouring,
That sometimes kill and always freeze
The high plenipotentiaries.
In Massachusetts all the way
From Boston down to Buzzards Bay
They feed you till you want to die
On rhubarb pie and pumpkin pie,
And horrible huckleberry pie,
And when you summon strength to cry,
'What is there else that I can try?'
They stare at you in mild surprise
And serve you other kinds of pies.
And I with these mine eyes have seen
A dreadful stuff called Margarine
Consumed by men in Bethnal Green.
But I myself that here complain
Confess restriction quite in vain.
I feel my native courage fail
To see a Gascon eat a snail;
I dare not ask abroad for tea;
No cannibal can dine with me;
And all the world is torn and rent
By varying views on nutriment.
And yet upon the other hand,
De gustibus non disputand—
                                    —*Um.*

THE BAD CHILD'S BOOK OF BEASTS

DEDICATION

To
Master Evelyn Bell
of Oxford

Evelyn Bell
I love you well.

INTRODUCTION

I call you bad, my little child,
   Upon the title page,
Because a manner rude and wild
   Is common at your age.

The Moral of this priceless work
   (If rightly understood)
Will make you—from a little Turk—
   Unnaturally good.

Do not as evil children do,
   Who on the slightest grounds
Will imitate the Kangaroo,
   With wild unmeaning bounds:

Do not as children badly bred,
   Who eat like little Hogs,
And when they have to go to bed
   Will whine like Puppy Dogs:

Who take their manners from the Ape,
   Their habits from the Bear,
Indulge the loud unseemly jape,
   And never brush their hair.

But so control your actions that
   Your friends may all repeat.
'This child is dainty as the Cat,
   And as the Owl discreet.'

THE YAK

As a friend to the children commend me the Yak.
  You will find it exactly the thing:
It will carry and fetch, you can ride on its back,
  Or lead it about with a string.

The Tartar who dwells on the plains of Thibet
  (A desolate region of snow)
Has for centuries made it a nursery pet,
  And surely the Tartar should know!

Then tell your papa where the Yak can be got,
  And if he is awfully rich
He will buy you the creature—or else he will *not*.
  (I cannot be positive which.)

THE POLAR BEAR

The Polar Bear is unaware
  Of cold that cuts me through:
For why? He has a coat of hair.
  I wish I had one too!

THE LION

The Lion, the Lion, he dwells in the waste,
He has a big head and a very small waist;
But his shoulders are stark, and his jaws they are grim,
And a good little child will not play with him.

THE TIGER

The Tiger on the other hand, is kittenish and mild,
He makes a pretty playfellow for any little child;
And mothers of large families (who claim to common sense)
Will find a Tiger well repay the trouble and expense.

THE DROMEDARY

The Dromedary is a cheerful bird:
I cannot say the same about the Kurd.

THE WHALE

The Whale that wanders round the Pole
  Is not a table fish.
You cannot bake or boil him whole
  Nor serve him in a dish;

But you may cut his blubber up
  And melt it down for oil,
And so replace the colza bean
  (A product of the soil).

These facts should all be noted down
  And ruminated on,
By every boy in Oxford town
  Who wants to be a Don.

THE HIPPOPOTAMUS

I shoot the Hippopotamus
With bullets made of platinum,
Because if I use leaden ones
His hide is sure to flatten 'em.

THE DODO

The Dodo used to walk around,
    And take the sun and air.
The sun yet warms his native ground—
    The Dodo is not there!

The voice which used to squawk and squeak
    Is now for ever dumb—
Yet may you see his bones and beak
    All in the Mu-se-um.

THE MARMOZET

The species Man and Marmozet
    Are intimately linked;
The Marmozet survives as yet,
    But Men are all extinct.

THE CAMELOPARD

The Camelopard, it is said
    By travellers (who never lie),
He cannot stretch out straight in bed
    Because he is so high.
The clouds surround his lofty head,
    His hornlets touch the sky.

How shall I hunt this quadruped?
    I cannot tell! Not I!
I'll buy a little parachute
    (A common parachute with wings),
I'll fill it full of arrowroot
    And other necessary things,

And I will slay this fearful brute
With stones and sticks and guns and slings.

THE LEARNED FISH

This learned Fish has not sufficient brains
To go into the water when it rains.

THE ELEPHANT

When people call this beast to mind
    They marvel more and more
At such a LITTLE tail behind,
    So LARGE a trunk before.

THE BIG BABOON

The Big Baboon is found upon
    The plains of Cariboo:
He goes about with nothing on
    (A shocking thing to do).

But if he dressed respectably
    And let his whiskers grow,
How like this Big Baboon would be
    To Mister So-and-so!

THE RHINOCEROS

Rhinoceros, your hide looks all undone,
You do not take my fancy in the least:
You have a horn where other brutes have none:
    Rhinoceros, you are an ugly beast.

THE FROG

Be kind and tender to the Frog,
    And do not call him names,
As 'Slimy skin', or 'Polly-wog',
    Or likewise 'Ugly James',
Or 'Gap-a-grin', or 'Toad-gone-wrong',
    Or 'Billy Bandy-knees':

The Frog is justly sensitive
    To epithets like these.
No animal will more repay
    A treatment kind and fair;
At least so lonely people say
Who keep a frog (and, by the way,
They are extremely rare).

MORE BEASTS FOR WORSE CHILDREN

DEDICATION

To

Miss Alice Wolcott Brinley

of Philadelphia

INTRODUCTION

The parents of the learned child
   (His father and his mother)
Were utterly aghast to note
The facts he would at random quote
On creatures curious, rare and wild;
   And wondering, asked each other:

'An idle little child like this,
   How is it that he knows
What years of close analysis
   Are powerless to disclose?

'Our brains are trained, our books are big,
   And yet we always fail
To answer why the Guinea-pig
   Is born without a tail.

'Or why the Wanderoo* should rant
   In wild, unmeaning rhymes,
Whereas the Indian Elephant
   Will only read *The Times*.

'Perhaps he found a way to slip
   Unnoticed to the Zoo,
And gave the Pachyderm a tip,
   Or pumped the Wanderoo.

'Or even by an artful plan
   Deceived our watchful eyes,
And interviewed the Pelican,
   Who is extremely wise.'

'Oh! no,' said he, in humble tone,
   With shy but conscious look,
'Such facts I never could have known
   But for this little book.'

* Sometimes called the 'Lion-tailed or tufted Baboon of Ceylon'.

THE PYTHON

A Python I should not advise—
It needs a doctor for its eyes,
And has the measles yearly.
However, if you feel inclined
To get one (to improve your mind,
And not from fashion merely),
Allow no music near its cage;
And when it flies into a rage
Chastise it, most severely.

I had an aunt in Yucatan
Who bought a Python from a man
   And kept it for a pet.
She died, because she never knew
Those simple little rules and few—
   The Snake is living yet.

THE WELSH MUTTON

The Cambrian Welsh or Mountain Sheep
   Is of the Ovine race,
His conversation is not deep,
   But then—observe his face!

THE PORCUPINE

What! would you slap the Porcupine?
    Unhappy child—desist!
Alas! that any friend of mine
    Should turn Tupto-philist.*

To strike the meanest and the least
    Of creatures is a sin,
How much more bad to beat a beast
    With prickles on its skin.

* From τυπτω = I strike; Φιλεω = I love; one that loves to strike. The word is not found in classical Greek, nor does it occur among the writers of the Renaissance—nor anywhere else.

THE SCORPION

The Scorpion is as black as soot,
    He dearly loves to bite;
He is a most unpleasant brute
    To find in bed, at night.

THE CROCODILE

Whatever our faults, we can always engage
That no fancy or fable shall sully our page,
   So take note of what follows, I beg.
This creature so grand and august in its age,
   In its youth is hatched out of an egg.
And oft in some far Coptic town
The Missionary sits him down
   To breakfast by the Nile:
The heart beneath his priestly gown
   Is innocent of guile;
When suddenly the rigid frown
Of Panic is observed to drown
   His customary smile.

Why does he start and leap amain,
And scour the sandy Libyan plain
Like one that wants to catch a train,
Or wrestles with internal pain?
Because he finds his egg contain—
Green, hungry, horrible and plain—
   An Infant Crocodile.

THE VULTURE

The Vulture eats between his meals,
   And that's the reason why
He very, very rarely feels
   As well as you and I.

His eye is dull, his head is bald,
   His neck is growing thinner.
Oh! what a lesson for us all
   To only eat at dinner!

THE BISON

The Bison is vain, and (I write it with pain)
    The Doormat you see on his head
Is not, as some learned professors maintain,
The opulent growth of a genius' brain;
    But is sewn on with needle and thread.

THE VIPER

Yet another great truth I record in my verse,
That some Vipers are venomous, some the reverse;
    A fact you may prove if you try,
By procuring two Vipers, and letting them bite;
With the *first* you are only the worse for a fright,
    But after the *second* you die.

THE LLAMA

The Llama is a woolly sort of fleecy hairy goat,
With an indolent expression and an undulating throat
    Like an unsuccessful literary man.
And I know the place he lives in (or at least—I think I do)
It is Ecuador, Brazil or Chili—possibly Peru;
    You must find it in the Atlas if you can.
The Llama of the Pampasses you never should confound
(In spite of a deceptive similarity of sound)
    With the Lhama who is Lord of Turkestan.
For the former is a beautiful and valuable beast,
But the latter is not lovable nor useful in the least;
And the Ruminant is preferable surely to the Priest
Who battens on the woeful superstitions of the East,
    The Mongol of the Monastery of Shan.

THE CHAMOIS

The Chamois inhabits
Lucerne, where his habits
  (Though why I have not an idea-r)
Give him sudden short spasms
On the brink of deep chasms,
    And he lives in perpetual fear.

THE FROZEN MAMMOTH

This Creature, though rare, is still found to the East
Of the Northern Siberian Zone.
It is known to the whole of that primitive group
That the carcass will furnish an excellent soup,
    Though the cooking it offers one drawback at least
      (Of a serious nature I own):
If the skin be *but punctured* before it is boiled,
Your confection is wholly and utterly spoiled.
And hence (on account of the size of the beast)
    The dainty is nearly unknown.

THE MICROBE

The Microbe is so very small
You cannot make him out at all,
But many sanguine people hope
To see him through a microscope.
His jointed tongue that lies beneath
A hundred curious rows of teeth;
His seven tufted tails with lots
Of lovely pink and purple spots,
On each of which a pattern stands,
Composed of forty separate bands;
His eyebrows of a tender green;
All these have never yet been seen—
But Scientists, who ought to know,
Assure us that they must be so . . .
Oh! let us never, never doubt
What nobody is sure about!

NUNQUAM FIDELIS

LORD ROEHAMPTON

During a late election Lord
Roehampton strained a vocal chord
From shouting, very loud and high,
To lots and lots of people why
The Budget in his own opin-
Ion should not be allowed to win.
He sought a Specialist, who said:
'You have a swelling in the head:
Your Larynx is a thought relaxed
And you are greatly over-taxed.'
'I am indeed! On every side!'
The Earl (for such he was) replied
In hoarse excitement . . . 'Oh! My Lord,
You jeopardise your vocal chord!'
Broke in the worthy Specialist.
'Come! Here's the treatment! I insist!
To Bed! to Bed! And do not speak
A single word till Wednesday week,
When I will come and set you free
(If you are cured) and take my fee.'
On Wednesday week the Doctor hires
A Brand-new Car with Brand-new Tyres
And Brand-new Chauffeur all complete
For visiting South Audley Street.

*

But what is this? No Union Jack
Floats on the Stables at the back!
No Toffs escorting Ladies fair
Perambulate the Gay Parterre.
A 'Scutcheon hanging lozenge-wise
And draped in crape appals his eyes
Upon the mansion's ample door,
To which he wades through heaps of Straw,*

* This is the first and only time
   That I have used this sort of Rhyme.

And which a Butler drowned in tears,
On opening but confirms his fears:
'Oh! Sir!—Prepare to hear the worst! . . .
Last night my kind old master burst.
And what is more, I doubt if he
Has left enough to pay your fee.
The Budget——' With a dreadful oath,
The Specialist, denouncing both
The Budget *and* the House of Lords,
Buzzed angrily Bayswaterwards.

*

And ever since, as I am told,
Gets it beforehand; and in gold.

LORD CALVIN

Lord Calvin thought the Bishops should not sit
As Peers of Parliament. And *argued* it!
In spite of which, for years, and years, and years,
They went on sitting with their fellow-peers.

LORD HENRY CHASE

What happened to Lord Henry Chase?
He got into a Libel Case!
The Daily Howl had said that he——
But could not prove it perfectly
To Judge or Jury's satisfaction:
His Lordship, therefore, won the action.
But, as the damages were small,
He gave them to a Hospital.

LORD HEYGATE

Lord Heygate had a troubled face,
His furniture was commonplace—
The sort of Peer who well might pass
For someone of the middle class.
I do not think you want to hear
About this unimportant Peer,
So let us leave him to discourse
About Lord Epsom and his horse.

LORD EPSOM

A horse Lord Epsom did bestride
With mastery and quiet pride.
He dug his spurs into its hide.
The Horse, discerning it was pricked,
Incontinently bucked and kicked,
A thing that no one could predict!

Lord Epsom clearly understood
The High-bred creature's nervous mood,
As only such a horseman could.
Dismounting, he was heard to say
That it was kinder to delay
His pleasure to a future day.
                    *
He had the Hunter led away.

LORD FINCHLEY

Lord Finchley tried to mend the Electric Light
Himself. It struck him dead: And serve him right!
It is the business of the wealthy man
To give employment to the artisan.

LORD ALI-BABA

Lord Ali-Baba was a Turk
Who hated every kind of work,
And would repose for hours at ease
With Houris seated on his knees.
A happy life!—Until, one day
Mossoo Alphonse Effendi Bey
(A Younger Turk: the very cream
And essence of the New Régime)
Dispelled this Oriental dream
By granting him a place at Court,
High Coffee-grinder to the Porte,
Unpaid: In which exalted Post
His Lordship yielded up the ghost.

LORD HIPPO

Lord Hippo suffered fearful loss
By putting money on a horse
Which he believed, if it were pressed,
Would run far faster than the rest:
For someone who was in the know
Had confidently told him so.
But on the morning of the race
It only took the *seventh* place!

Picture the Viscount's great surprise!
He scarcely could believe his eyes!
He sought the Individual who
Had laid him odds at 9 to 2,
Suggesting as a useful tip
That they should enter Partnership
And put to joint account the debt
Arising from his foolish bet.
But when the Bookie—oh! my word,
I only wish you could have heard
The way he roared he did not think,
And hoped that they might strike him pink!
Lord Hippo simply turned and ran
From this infuriated man.
Despairing, maddened and distraught
He utterly collapsed and sought
His sire, the Earl of Potamus,
And brokenly addressed him thus:
'Dread Sire—today—at Ascot—I . . .'
His genial parent made reply:
'Come! Come! Come! Come! Don't look so glum!
Trust your Papa and name the sum . . .
WHAT? . . . *Fifteen hundred thousand?* . . . Hum!
However . . . stiffen up, you wreck;
Boys will be boys—so here's the cheque!'
Lord Hippo, feeling deeply—well,
More grateful than he cared to tell—
Punted the lot on Little Nell:
And got a telegram at dinner
To say that he had backed the Winner!

LORD UNCLE TOM

Lord Uncle Tom was different from
    What other nobles are.
For they are yellow or pink, I think,
    But he was black as tar.

He had his Father's debonair
    And rather easy pride:
But his complexion and his hair
    Were from the mother's side.

He often mingled in debate
    And latterly displayed
Experience of peculiar weight
    Upon the Cocoa trade.

But now He speaks no more. The BILL
    Which he could not abide,
It preyed upon his mind until
    He sickened, paled, and died.

LORD CANTON

The reason that the Present Lord Canton
Succeeded lately to his Brother John
Was that his Brother John, the elder son,
Died rather suddenly at forty-one.
The insolence of an Italian guide
Appears to be the reason that he died.

LORD ABBOTT

Lord Abbott's coronet was far too small,
So small, that as he sauntered down Whitehall
Even the youthful Proletariat
(Who probably mistook it for a Hat)
Remarked on its exiguous extent.
Here is a picture of the incident.

LORD LUCKY

Lord Lucky, by a curious fluke,
Became a most important duke.
From living in a vile Hotel
A long way east of Camberwell
He rose in less than half an hour,
To riches, dignity and power.
It happened in the following way:
The Real Duke went out one day
To shoot with several people, one
Of whom had never used a gun.
This gentleman (a Mr Meyer
Of Rabley Abbey, Rutlandshire),
As he was scrambling through the brake,
Discharged his weapon by mistake,
And plugged about an ounce of lead
Piff-bang into his Grace's Head——
Who naturally fell down dead.
His Heir, Lord Ugly, roared, 'You Brute!
Take that to teach you how to shoot!'
Whereat he volleyed, left and right;
But being somewhat short of sight,
His right-hand Barrel only got
The second heir, Lord Poddleplot;
The while the left-hand charge (or choke)
Accounted for another bloke,
Who stood with an astounded air
Bewildered by the whole affair
—And was the third remaining heir.
After the Execution (which
Is something rare among the Rich)
Lord Lucky, while of course he needed
Some help to prove his claim, succeeded.
—But after his succession, though
All this was over years ago,
He only once indulged the whim
Of asking Meyer to lunch with him.

A MORAL ALPHABET

A MORAL ALPHABET

A stands for Archibald who told no lies,
And got this lovely volume for a prize.
The Upper School had combed and oiled their hair,
And all the Parents of the Boys were there.
In words that ring like thunder through the Hall,
Draw tears from some and loud applause from all—
The Pedagogue, with Pardonable Joy,
Bestows the Gift upon the Radiant Boy:
'Accept the Noblest Work produced as yet'
(Says he) 'upon the English Alphabet;
Next term I shall examine you, to find
If you have read it thoroughly. So mind!'
And while the Boys and Parents cheered so loud,
That out of doors a large and anxious crowd
Had gathered and was blocking up the street,
The admirable child resumed his seat.

MORAL

Learn from this justly irritating Youth,
To brush your Hair and Teeth and tell the Truth.

B stands for Bear. When Bears are seen
    Approaching in the distance,
Make up your mind at once between
    Retreat and Armed Resistance.

A Gentleman remained to fight—
    With what result for him?
The Bear, with ill-concealed delight,
    Devoured him, Limb by Limb.

Another Person turned and ran;
    He ran extremely hard:
The Bear was faster than the Man,
    And beat him by a yard.

MORAL

Decisive action in the hour of need
Denotes the Hero, but does not succeed.

C stands for Cobra; when the Cobra bites
An Indian Judge, the Judge spends restless nights.

MORAL

This creature, though disgusting and appalling,
Conveys no kind of Moral worth recalling.

D

The Dreadful Dinotherium he
Will have to do his best for D.
The early world observed with awe
His back, indented like a saw.
His look was gay, his voice was strong;
His tail was neither short nor long;
His trunk, or elongated nose,
Was not so large as some suppose;
His teeth, as all the world allows,
Were graminivorous, like a cow's.
He therefore should have wished to pass
Long peaceful nights upon the Grass,
But being mad the brute preferred
To roost in branches, like a bird.*
A creature heavier than a whale,
You see at once, could hardly fail
To suffer badly when he slid
And tumbled (as he always did).
His fossil, therefore, comes to light
All broken up: and serve him right.

MORAL

If you were born to walk the ground,
Remain there; do not fool around.

* We have good reason to suppose
  He did so, from his claw-like toes.

E stands for Egg.

MORAL

The Moral of this verse
Is applicable to the Young. Be terse.

F for a Family taking a walk
   In Arcadia Terrace, no doubt:
The parents indulge in intelligent talk,
   While the children they gambol about.

At a quarter past six they return to their tea,
Of a kind that would hardly be tempting to me,
   Though my appetite passes belief.
There is Jam, Ginger Beer, Buttered Toast, Marmalade,
With a Cold Leg of Mutton and Warm Lemonade,
And a large Pigeon Pie very skilfully made
   To consist almost wholly of Beef.

MORAL

A Respectable Family taking the air
   Is a subject on which I could dwell;
It contains all the morals that ever there were,
   And it sets an example as well.

G stands for Gnu, whose weapons of Defence
Are long, sharp, curling Horns, and Common-sense.
To these he adds a Name so short and strong
That even Hardy Boers pronounce it wrong.
How often on a bright Autumnal day
The Pious people of Pretoria say,
'Come, let us hunt the——' Then no more is heard
But Sounds of Strong Men struggling with a word.
Meanwhile, the distant Gnu with grateful eyes
Observes his opportunity, and flies.

MORAL

Child, if you have a rummy kind of name,
Remember to be thankful for the same.

H was a Horseman who rode to the meet,
And talked of the Pads of the fox as his 'feet'—
An error which furnished subscribers with grounds
For refusing to make him a Master of Hounds.
He gave way thereupon to so fearful a rage,
That he sold up his Stable and went on the Stage,
And had all the success that a man could desire
In creating the part of 'The Old English Squire'.

MORAL

In the Learned Professions, a person should know
The advantage of having two strings to his bow.

I the Poor Indian, justly called 'The Poor',
He has to eat his Dinner off the floor.

MORAL

The Moral these delightful lines afford
Is: 'Living cheaply is its own reward.'

J stands for James, who thought it immaterial
To pay his taxes, Local or Imperial.
In vain the Mother wept, the Wife implored,
James only yawned as though a trifle bored.
The Tax Collector called again, but he
Was met with persiflage and Repartee.
When James was hauled before the learned Judge,
Who lectured him, he loudly whispered, 'Fudge!'
The Judge was startled from his usual calm,
He struck the desk before him with his palm,
And roared in tones to make the boldest quail,
'*J stands for James*, IT ALSO STANDS FOR JAIL.'
And therefore, on a dark and dreadful day,
Policemen came and took him all away.

MORAL

The fate of James is typical, and shows
   How little mercy people can expect
Who will not pay their taxes; (saving those
   To which they conscientiously object).

K for the Klondyke, a Country of Gold,
Where the winters are often excessively cold;
Where the lawn every morning is covered with rime,
And skating continues for years at a time.
Do you think that a Climate can conquer the grit
Of the Sons of the West? Not a bit! Not a bit!
When the weather looks nippy, the bold Pioneers
Put on two pairs of Stockings and cover their ears,
And roam through the drear Hyperborean dales
With a vast apparatus of Buckets and Pails;
Or wander through wild Hyperborean glades
With Hoes, Hammers, Pickaxes, Mattocks and Spades.
There are some who give rise to exuberant mirth

By turning up nothing but bushels of earth,
While those who have little cause excellent fun
By attempting to pilfer from those who have none.
At times the reward they will get for their pains
Is to strike very tempting auriferous veins;
Or, a shaft being sunk for some miles in the ground,
Not infrequently nuggets of value are found.
They bring us the gold when their labours are ended,
And we—after thanking them prettily—spend it.

MORAL

Just you work for Humanity, never you mind
If Humanity seems to have left you behind.

L was a Lady, Advancing in Age,
   Who drove in her carriage and six,
With a Couple of Footmen, a Coachman and Page,
   Who were all of them regular bricks.
If the Coach ran away, or was smashed by a Dray,
   Or got into collisions and blocks,
The Page, with a courtesy rare for his years,
Would leap to the ground with inspiriting cheers,
While the Footman allayed her legitimate fears,
   And the Coachman sat tight on his box.
At night as they met round an excellent meal,
   They would take it in turn to observe:
'What a Lady indeed! . . . what a presence to feel! . . .'
   'What a woman to worship and serve! . . .'
But, perhaps, the most poignant of all their delights
   Was to stand in a rapturous Dream
When she spoke to them kindly on Saturday Nights
   And said 'They deserved her Esteem.'

MORAL

Now observe the Reward of these dutiful lives:
   At the end of their Loyal Career

They each had a Lodge at the end of the drives,
    And she left them a Hundred a Year.
Remember from this to be properly vexed
    When the newspaper editors say
That 'The type of society shown in the Text
    Is rapidly passing away.'

M was a Millionaire who sat at Table,
    And ate like this—as long as he was able;
At half past twelve the waiters turned him out:
    He lived impoverished and died of gout.

MORAL

Disgusting exhibition! Have a care
When, later on, you are a Millionaire,
To rise from table feeling you could still
Take something more, and not be really ill.

N stands for Ned, Maria's younger brother,
Who, walking one way, chose to gaze the other.
In Blandford Square—a crowded part of town—
Two People on a tandem knocked him down;
Whereat a Motor Car, with warning shout,
Ran right on top and turned him inside out:
The damages that he obtained from these
Maintained him all his life in cultured ease.

MORAL

The law protects you. Go your gentle way:
The Other Man has always got to Pay.

O stands for Oxford. Hail! salubrious seat
Of learning! Academical Retreat!
Home of my Middle Age! Malarial Spot
Which People call Medeeval (though it's not).
The marshes in the neighbourhood can vie
With Cambridge, but the town itself is dry,
And serves to make a kind of Fold or Pen
Wherein to herd a lot of Learned Men.
Were I to write but half of what they know,
It would exhaust the space reserved for 'O';
And, as my book must not be over big,
I turn at once to 'P', which stands for Pig.

MORAL

Be taught by this to speak with moderation
Of places where, with decent application,
One gets a good, sound, middle-class education.

P stands for Pig, as I remarked before,
A second cousin to the Huge Wild Boar.
But Pigs are civilised, while Huge Wild Boars
Live savagely, at random, out of doors,
And, in their coarse contempt for dainty foods,
Subsist on Truffles, which they find in woods.
Not so the cultivated Pig, who feels
The need of several courses at his meals,
But wrongly thinks it does not matter whether
He takes them one by one or all together.
Hence, Pigs devour, from lack of self-respect,
What Epicures would certainly eject.

MORAL

Learn from the Pig to take whatever Fate
Or Elder Persons heap upon your plate.

Q for Quinine, which children take
With Jam and little bits of cake.

MORAL

How idiotic! Can Quinine
Replace Cold Baths and Sound Hygiene?

R the Reviewer, reviewing my book,
At which he had barely intended to look;
But the very first lines upon 'A' were enough
To convince him the *Verses* were excellent stuff.
So he wrote, without stopping, for several days
In terms of extreme but well-merited Praise.
To quote but one Passage: 'No Person' (says he)
'Will be really content without purchasing three,
While a Parent will send for a dozen or more,
And strew them about on the Nursery Floor.
The Versification might call for some strictures
Were it not for its singular wit; while the Pictures,
Tho' the handling of line is a little defective,
Make up amply in *verve* what they lack in perspective.'

MORAL

The habit of constantly telling the Truth
Will lend an additional lustre to Youth.

S stands for Snail, who, though he be the least,
Is not an uninstructive Hornèd Beast.
His eyes are on his Horns, and when you shout
Or tickle them, the Horns go in and out.
Had Providence seen proper to endow

The furious Unicorn or sober Cow
With such a gift the one would never now
Appear so commonplace on Coats of Arms.
And what a fortune for our failing farms
If circus managers, with wealth untold,
Would take the Cows for half their weight in gold!

Learn from the Snail to take reproof with patience,
And not put out your Horns on all occasions.

T for the Genial Tourist, who resides
In Peckham, where he writes Italian Guides.

Learn from this information not to cavil
At slight mistakes in books on foreign travel.

U for the Upas Tree, that casts a blight
On those that pull their sisters' hair, and fight.
But oh! the Good! They wander undismayed,
And (as the Subtle Artist has portrayed)
Dispend the golden hours at play beneath its shade.*

Dear Reader, if you chance to catch a sight
Of Upas Trees, betake yourself to flight.

* A friend of mine, a Botanist, believes
  The Good can even browse upon its leaves.
  I doubt it . . .

V for the unobtrusive Volunteer,
Who fills the Armies of the World with fear.

Seek with the Volunteer to put aside
The empty Pomp of Military Pride.

W

My little victim, let me trouble you
To fix your active mind on W.
The WATERBEETLE here shall teach
A sermon far beyond your reach:
He flabbergasts the Human Race
By gliding on the water's face
With ease, celerity, and grace;
But if he ever stopped to think
Of how he did it, he would sink.

Don't ask Questions!

X

No reasonable little Child expects
A Grown-up Man to make a rhyme on X.

These verses teach a clever child to find
Excuse for doing all that he's inclined.

Y stands for Youth (it would have stood for Yak,
But that I wrote about him two years back).
Youth is the pleasant springtime of our days,
As Dante so mellifluously says
(Who always speaks of Youth with proper praise).
You have not got to Youth, but when you do
You'll find what He and I have said is true.

MORAL

Youth's excellence should teach the Modern Wit
First to be Young, and then to boast of it.

Z for this Zébu, who (like all Zebús)*
Is held divine by scrupulous Hindoos.

MORAL

Idolatry, as you are well aware,
Is highly reprehensible. But there,
We needn't bother—when we get to Z
Our interest in the Alphabet is dead.

* Von Kettner writes it 'Zébu'; Wurst 'Zebú':
  I split the difference and use the two.

LADIES AND GENTLEMEN

THE GARDEN PARTY

The Rich arrived in pairs
And also in Rolls Royces;
They talked of their affairs
In loud and strident voices.

(The Husbands and the Wives
Of this select society
Lead independent lives
Of infinite variety.)

The Poor arrived in Fords,
Whose features they resembled;
They laughed to see so many Lords
And Ladies all assembled.

The People in Between
Looked underdone and harassed,
And out of place and mean,
And horribly embarrassed.

For the hoary social curse
Gets hoarier and hoarier,
And it stinks a trifle worse
                Than in
The days of Queen Victoria,
                when
They married and gave in marriage,
They danced at the County Ball,
And some of them kept a carriage.
AND THE FLOOD DESTROYED THEM ALL.

WILLIAM SHAND

There was a man called WILLIAM SHAND,
He had the habit of command,
And when subordinates would shout
He used to bang them all about.
It happened, by a turn of Fate,
Himself became subordinate,
Through being passenger upon
A liner, going to Ceylon.
One day, as they were in the Red
(Or Libyan) Sea, the Captain said:
'I think it's coming on to blow.
Let everybody go below!'
But William Shand said: 'Not for me.
I'm going to stop on deck!' said he.
The Captain, wounded in his pride,
Summoned the Second Mate aside
And whispered: 'Surely Mr Shand
Must be extremely rich by land?'
'No,' said the Mate, 'when last ashore
I watched him. He is rather poor.'
'Ho!' cried the Captain. 'Stands it thus?
And shall the knave make mock of us?
I'll teach him to respect his betters.
Here, Bo'swain! Put the man in fetters!'
In fetters therefore William lay
Until the liner reached Bombay,
When he was handed to the court
Which deals with cases of the sort
In that uncomfortable port;
Which promptly hanged him out of hand.
Such was the fate of William Shand.

MORAL

The moral is that people must,
If they are poor, obey or bust.

THE THREE RACES

I

Behold, my child, the Nordic Man
And be as like him as you can.
His legs are long; his mind is slow;
His hair is lank and made of tow.

II

And here we have the Alpine Race.
Oh! What a broad and foolish face!
His skin is of a dirty yellow,
He is a most unpleasant fellow.

III

The most degraded of them all
Mediterranean we call.
His hair is crisp, and even curls,
And he is saucy with the girls.

OBITER DICTA

I

SIR HENRY WAFFLE K C (*continuing*)
Sir Anthony Habberton, Justice and Knight,
Was enfeoffed of two acres of land
And it doesn't sound much till you hear that the site
Was a strip to the South of the Strand.

HIS LORDSHIP (*Obiter Dictum*)
A strip to the South of the Strand
Is a good situation for land.
It is healthy and dry
And sufficiently high
And convenient on every hand.

II

SIR HENRY WAFFLE K C (*continuing*)
Now Sir Anthony, shooting in Timberley Wood,
Was imprudent enough to take cold;
And he died without warning at six in the morning,
Because he was awfully old.

HIS LORDSHIP (*Obiter Dictum*)
I have often been credibly told
That when people are awfully old
Though cigars are a curse
And strong waters are worse
There is nothing so fatal as cold.

III

SIR HENRY WAFFLE K C (*continuing*)
But Archibald answered on hearing the news:
'I never move out till I must.'
Which was all very jolly for *Cestui que Use*
But the Devil for *Cestui que Trust*.

HIS LORDSHIP (*Obiter Dictum*)
The office of *Cestui que Trust*
Is reserved for the learned and just.
Any villain you choose
May be *Cestui que Use*,
But a Lawyer for *Cestui que Trust*.

IV

SIR HENRY WAFFLE K C (*continuing*)
Now the ruling laid down in *Regina v. Brown*
May be cited . . .

HIS LORDSHIP (*rising energetically*)
You're wrong! It may not!
I've strained all my powers
For some thirty-six hours
To unravel this pestilent rot.

THE WHOLE COURT (*rising and singing in chorus*)
Your Lordship is sound to the core.
It is nearly a quarter to four.
We've had quite enough of this horrible stuff
And we don't want to hear any more!

LITTLE SILLY MAN (*rising at the back of the Court*)
Your Lordship is perfectly right.
He can't go on rhyming all night.
I suggest . . .
    (*He is gagged, bound and dragged off to a Dungeon.*)

THE STATESMAN

I knew a man who used to say,
Not once but twenty times a day,
That in the turmoil and the strife
(His very words) of Public Life
The thing of ultimate effect
Was Character—not Intellect.
He therefore was at strenuous pains
To atrophy his puny brains
And registered success in this
Beyond the dreams of avarice,
Till, when he had at last become
Blind, paralytic, deaf and dumb,
Insensible and cretinous,
He was admitted ONE OF US.
They therefore, (meaning Them by 'They')
His colleagues of the N C A,
The T U C, the I L P
Appointed him triumphantly
To bleed the taxes of a clear
200,000 Francs a year
(Swiss), as the necessary man
For Conferences at Lausanne,
Geneva, Basle, Locarno, Berne:
A salary which he will earn,
Yes—*earn* I say—until he Pops,
Croaks, passes in his checks and Stops:
When he will be remembered for
A week, a month, or even more.

THE AUTHOR

There is a literary man,
Whose name is Herbert Keanes:
His coat is lined with astrakhan.
He lives on private means.

His house is in St James's Square
(Which I could not afford).
His head is strong but short of hair,
His Uncle is a Lord.

This Uncle loves him like a son
And has been heard to vow
He will be famous later on
And even might be now.

And he has left him in his will
New Boyton, Hatton Strand,
Long Stokely, Pilly-on-the-Hill,
And Lower Sandiland.

He is not dead, but when he dies
This wealth will all accrue,
Unless the old gafoozler lies,
O Herbert Keanes, to you!

The Son? The Son whom *She* alone
Could bear to such a sire,
The son of Lady Jane O'Hone
And Henry Keanes Esquire.

First with a private tutor, then
At Eton Herbert Keanes,
Like other strong successful men,
Was nurtured in his teens.

To curious dons he next would pay
His trifling entrance fee,
And was accepted, strange to say,
By those of Trinity:

Tall Trinity whereby the Cam
Its awful torrent rolls,
But there!—I do not care a damn,
It might have been All Souls.

Has sat for Putticombe in Kent
But lost the seat he won
By boldly saying what he meant
Though meaning he had none.

Has written 'Problems of the Poor',
'The Future of Japan'
And 'Musings by Killarney's Shore'
And 'What Indeed is Man?'

And 'Flowers and Fruit' (a book of verse)
'The Ethics of St Paul',
'Was there a Peter?' (rather worse)
And 'Nero' (worst of all).

Clubs: Handy Dandy, Beagle's, Tree's,
Pitt, Palmerston, Riviere,
The Walnut Box, Empedocles,
Throgmorton, Pot o' Beer.

(The last for its bohemian lists
Wherein he often meets
Old Wasters, Poets, Communists,
And Ladies from the Streets.)

A strong Protectionist, believes
In everything but Heaven.
For entertainment, dines, receives,
Unmarried, fifty-seven.

THE EXAMPLE

John Henderson, an unbeliever,
Had lately lost his Joie de Vivre
From reading far too many books.
He went about with gloomy looks;
Despair inhabited his breast
And made the man a perfect pest.
Not so his sister, Mary Lunn,
She had a whacking lot of fun!
Though unbelieving as a beast
She didn't worry in the least,
But drank as hard as she was able
And sang and danced upon the table;
And when she met her brother Jack
She used to smack him on the back
So smartly as to make him jump,
And cry, 'What-ho! You've got the hump!'
A phrase which, more than any other,
Was gall and wormwood to her brother;

For, having an agnostic mind,
He was exceedingly refined.
The Christians, a declining band,
Would point with monitory hand
To Henderson his desperation,
To Mary Lunn her dissipation,
And often mutter, 'Mark my words!
Something will happen to those birds!'
Which came to pass: for Mary Lunn
Died suddenly, at ninety-one,
Of Psittacosis, not before
Becoming an appalling bore.
While Henderson, I'm glad to state,
Though naturally celibate,
Married an intellectual wife
Who made him lead the Higher life
And wouldn't give him any wine;
Whereby he fell in a decline,
And, at the time of writing this,
Is suffering from paralysis,
The which we hear with no surprise,
Will shortly end in his demise.

MORAL

The moral is (it is indeed!)
You mustn't monkey with the Creed.

THE MODERN TRAVELLER

THE MODERN TRAVELLER

The *Daily Menace*, I presume?
Forgive the litter in the room.
I can't explain to you
How out of place a man like me
Would be without the things you see—
The Shields and Assegais and odds
And ends of little savage gods.
Be seated; take a pew.
(Excuse the phrase. I'm rather rough,
And—pardon me!—but have you got
A pencil? I've another here:
The one that you have brought, I fear,
Will not be long enough.)
And so the Public want to hear
About the expedition
From which I recently returned:
Of how the Fetish Tree was burned;
Of how we struggled to the coast,
And lost our ammunition;
How we retreated, side by side;
And how, like Englishmen, we died.
Well, as you know, I hate to boast,
And, what is more, I can't abide
A popular position.
I told the Duke the other day
The way I felt about it.
He answered courteously—'Oh!'
An Editor (who had an air
Of what the Dutch call *savoir faire*)
Said, 'Mr Rooter, you are right,
And nobody can doubt it.'
The Duchess murmured, 'Very true.'
Her comments may be brief and few,
But very seldom trite.

Still, representing as you do
A public and a point of view,
I'll give you leave to jot
A few remarks—a very few—
But understand that this is not
A formal interview.
And first of all, I will begin
By talking of Commander Sin.

II

Poor Henry Sin from quite a child,
I fear, was always rather wild;
    But all his faults were due
To something free and unrestrained,
That partly pleased and partly pained
    The people whom he knew.
Untaught (for what our times require),
Lazy, and something of a liar,
    He had a foolish way
Of always swearing (more or less);
    And, lastly, let us say
A little slovenly in dress,
A trifle prone to drunkenness;
A gambler also to excess,
    And never known to pay.
As for his clubs in London, he
Was pilled at ten, expelled from three.
A man Bohemian as could be—
    But really vicious? Oh, no!
When these are mentioned, all is said.
And then—Commander Sin is dead:
    De Mortuis cui bono?

Of course, the Public know I mean
To publish in the winter.
I mention the intention in
Connection with Commander Sin;
    The book is with the Printer.

And here, among the proofs, I find
The very thing I had in mind—
The portrait upon page thirteen.
Pray pause awhile, and mark
The wiry limbs, the vigorous mien,
The tangled hair and dark;
The glance imperative and hot,
    That takes a world by storm:
All these are in the plate, but what
You chiefly should observe is
The—Did you say his uniform
Betrayed a foreign service?

Of course, it does! He was not born
In little England! No!
Beyond the Cape, beyond the Horn,
Beyond Fernando Po,
In some far Isle he saw the light
That burns the torrid zone,
But where it lay was never quite
Indubitably known.
Himself inclined to Martinique,
His friends to Farralone.
But why of this discussion speak?
The Globe was all his own!
Oh! surely upon such a birth
No petty flag unfurled!
He was a citizen of earth,
A subject of the world!

As for the uniform he bore,
He won it in the recent war
Between Peru and Ecuador,
    And thoroughly he earned it.
Alone of all who at the time
Were serving sentences for crime,
Sin, during his incarceration
Had studied works on navigation;

And when the people learned it,
They promptly let him out of jail,
But on condition he should sail.

It marked an epoch, and you may
Recall the action in
A place called Quaxipotle bay?
Yes, both the navies ran away;
And yet, if Ecuador can say
That on the whole she won the day,
The fact is due to Sin.
The Fleet was hardly ten weeks out,
When somebody descried
The enemy. Sin gave a shout,
The Helmsmen put the ship about;
For, upon either side,
Tactics demanded a retreat.
Due west retired the foreign fleet,
But Sin he steered due east;
He muttered, 'They shall never meet.'
And when, towards the close of day,
The foemen were at least
Fifteen or twenty miles away,
He called his cabin-steward aft,
The boldest of his men;
He grasped them by the hand; he laughed
A fearless laugh, and then,
'Heaven help the right! Full steam ahead,
Fighting for fighting's sake,' he said.

Due west the foe—due east he steered.
Ah, me! the very stokers cheered,
And faces black with coal
And fuzzy with a five days' beard
Popped up, and yelled, and disappeared
Each in its little hole.
Long after they were out of sight,
Long after dark, throughout the night,

Throughout the following day,
He went on fighting all the time!
Not war, perhaps, but how sublime!

Just as he would have stepped ashore,
The President of Ecuador
Came on his quarterdeck;
Embraced him twenty times or more,
And gave him stripes and things galore,
Crosses and medals by the score,
And handed him a cheque—
And then a little speech he read.

'Of twenty years, your sentence said,
That you should serve—another week
(Alas! it shames me as I speak)
Was owing when you quitted.
In recognition of your nerve,
It gives me pleasure to observe
The time you still had got to serve
Is totally remitted.

'Instead of which these friends of mine'
(And here he pointed to a line
Of Colonels on the Quay)
'Have changed your sentence to a fine
Made payable to me.
No—do not thank me—not a word!
I am very glad to say
This little cheque is quite a third
Of what you have to pay.'

The crew they cheered and cheered again,
The simple loyal-hearted men!

Such deeds could never fail to be
Renowned throughout the west.
It was our cousins over sea

That loved the Sailor best—
Our Anglo-Saxon kith and kin,
They doted on Commander Sin,
And gave him a tremendous feast
The week before we started.
O'Hooligan, and Vonderbeast,
And Nicolazzi, and the rest,
Were simply broken-hearted.

They came and ate and cried, 'God speed!'
The Bill was very large indeed,
And paid for by an Anglo-Saxon
Who bore the sterling name of Jackson.
On this occasion Sin was seen
Toasting McKinley and the Queen.
The speech was dull, but not an eye,
Not even the champagne, was dry.

III

Now William Blood, or, as I still
Affectionately call him, Bill,
Was of a different stamp;
One who, in other ages born
Had turned to strengthen and adorn
The Senate or the Camp.
But Fortune, jealous and austere,
Had marked him for a great career
Of more congenial kind—
A sort of modern Buccaneer,
Commercial and refined.
Like all great men, his chief affairs
Were buying stocks and selling shares.
He occupied his mind
In buying them by day from men
Who needed ready cash, and then
At evening selling them again
To those with whom he dined.

But such a task could never fill
His masterful ambition.
That rapid glance, that iron will,
Disdained (and rightfully) to make
A profit here and there, or take
His two per cent commission.
His soul with nobler stuff was fraught;
The love of country, as it ought,
Haunted his every act and thought.
To that he lent his mighty powers,
To that he gave his waking hours,
Of that he dreamed in troubled sleep,
Till, after many years, the deep
    Imperial emotion,
That moves us like a martial strain,
Turned his Napoleonic brain
    To company promotion.

He failed, and it was better so:
    It made our expedition.
One day (it was a year ago)
He came on foot across the town,
And said his luck was rather down,
And would I lend him half-a-crown?
    I did, but on condition
(Drawn up in proper legal shape,
Witnessed and sealed, and tied with tape,
And costing two pound two)
That, 'If within the current year
He made a hundred thousand clear,'
He should accompany me in
A Project I had formed with Sin
    To go to Timbuctoo.
Later, we had a tiff because
I introduced another clause,
    Of which the general sense is,
That Blood, in the unlikely case
Of this adventure taking place,

Should pay the whole expenses.
Blood swore that he had never read
Or seen the clause. But Blood is dead.

Well, through a curious stroke of luck,
That very afternoon, he struck
    A new concern, in which,
By industry and honest ways,
He grew (to his eternal praise!)
In something less than sixty days
    Inordinately rich.

Let me describe what he became
    The day that he succeeded—
Though, in the searching light that Fame
Has cast on that immortal name,
    The task is hardly needed.

The world has very rarely seen
A deeper gulf than stood between
    The men who were my friends.
And, speaking frankly, I confess
They never cared to meet, unless
It served their private ends.

Sin loved the bottle, William gold;
'Twas Blood that bought and Sin that sold,
    In all their mutual dealings.
Blood never broke the penal laws;
Sin did it all the while, because
    He had the finer feelings.

Blood had his dreams, but Sin was mad:
While Sin was foolish, Blood was bad,
Sin, though I say it, was a cad.
    (And if the word arouses
Some criticism, pray reflect
How twisted was his intellect,

And what a past he had!)
But Blood was exquisitely bred,
    And always in the swim,
And people were extremely glad
    To ask him to their houses.
Be not too eager to condemn:
It was not he that hunted them,
    But they that hunted him.

In this fair world of culture made
For men of his peculiar trade,
Of all the many parts he played,
The part he grew to like the best
Was called 'the self-respecting guest'.
    And for that very reason
He found himself in great request
    At parties in the season,
Wherever gentlemen invest,
    From Chelsea to Mayfair.
From Lath and Stucco Gate, SW,
    To 90, Berkeley Square.
The little statesmen in the bud,
    The big provincial mayor,
    The man that owns a magazine,
    The authoress who might have been;
They always sent a card to Blood,
    And Blood was always there.
At every dinner, crush or rout,
A little whirlpool turned about
The form immovable and stout,
    That marked the Millionaire.
Sin (you remember) could not stay
In any club for half a day,
    When once his name was listed;
But Blood belonged to ninety-four,
And would have joined as many more
    Had any more existed.
Sin at a single game would lose

A little host of I O Us,
And often took the oath absurd
To break the punters or his word
    Before it was completed.
Blood was another pair of shoes:
A man of iron, cold and hard,
He very rarely touched a card,
But when he did he cheated.
Again the origin of Sin,
    Was doubtful and obscure;
Whereas, the Captain's origin
    Was absolutely sure.

A document affirms that he
Was born in 1853
Upon a German ship at sea,
    Just off the Grand Canary.
And though the log is rather free
And written too compactly,
We know the weather to a T,
The longitude to a degree,
The latitude exactly,
    And every detail is the same;
    We even know his Mother's name.
As to his father's occupation,
Creed, colour, character or nation,
    (On which the rumours vary);
He said himself concerning it,
With admirably caustic wit,
    'I think the Public would much rather
    Be sure of me than of my father.'

The contrast curiously keen
    Their characters could yield
Was most conspicuously seen
    Upon the Tented Field.
Was there by chance a native tribe
To cheat, cajole, corrupt, or bribe?—

In such conditions Sin would burn
    To plunge into the fray,
While Blood would run the whole concern
    From fifty miles away.

He had, wherever honours vain
Were weighed against material gain,
A judgement, practical and sane,
    Peculiarly his own.
In this connection let me quote
An interesting anecdote
    Not generally known.
Before he sailed he might have been
    (If he had thought it paid him)
A military man of note.
Her gracious Majesty the Queen
    Would certainly have made him,
In spite of his advancing years,
A Captain of the Volunteers.
A certain Person of the Sort
That has great influence at Court,
    Assured him it was so;
And said, 'It simply lies with you
To get this little matter through.
You pay a set of trifling fees
To me—at any time you please——'
Blood stopped him with a 'No!'
'This signal favour of the Queen's
Is very burdensome. It means
A smart Review (for all I know),
In which I am supposed to show
    Strategical ability:
And after that tremendous fights
And sleeping out on rainy nights,
    And much responsibility.
Thank you: I have my own position,
I need no parchment or commission,
And everyone who knows my name

Will call me "Captain" just the same.'
There was our leader in a phrase:
A man of strong decisive ways,
    But reticent* and grim.
Though not an Englishman, I own,
Perhaps it never will be known
    What England lost in him!

IV

The ship was dropping down the stream,
The Isle of Dogs was just abeam,
    And Sin and Blood and I
Saw Greenwich Hospital go past,
And gave a look—(for them the last)—
    Towards the London sky!
Ah! nowhere have I ever seen
A sky so pure and so serene!

Did we at length, perhaps, regret
    Our strange adventurous lot?
And were our eyes a trifle wet
With tears that we repressed, and yet
    Which started blinding hot?
Perhaps—and yet, I do not know,
For when we came to go below,
    We cheerfully admitted
That though there was a smell of paint
(And though a very just complaint
Had to be lodged against the food),
The cabin furniture was good
    And comfortably fitted.
And even out beyond the Nore
We did not ask to go ashore.

To turn to more congenial topics,
    I said a little while ago

* This reticence, which some have called hypocrisy
  Was but the sign of nature's aristocracy.

The food was very much below
The standard needed to prepare
Explorers for the special fare
Which all authorities declare
   Is needful in the tropics.
A Frenchman sitting next to us
Rejected the asparagus;
The turtle soup was often cold,
The ices hot, the omelettes old,
The coffee worse than I can tell;
And Sin (who had a happy knack
Of rhyming rapidly and well
Like Cyrano de Bergerac)
   Said '*Quant à moi, je n'aime pas*
   Du tout ce pâté de foie gras!'
But this fastidious taste
Succeeded in a startling way;
At Dinner on the following day
   They gave us Bloater Paste.
Well—hearty Pioneers and rough
   Should not be over nice;
I think these lines are quite enough,
   And hope they will suffice
To make the Caterers observe
The kind of person whom they serve——
*

And yet I really must complain
About the Company's Champagne!
   This most expensive kind of wine
In England is a matter
Of pride or habit when we dine
   (Presumably the latter).
Beneath an equatorial sky
You *must* consume it or you die;
And stern indomitable men
Have told me, time and time again,
'The nuisance of the tropics is
The sheer necessity of fizz.'

Consider then the carelessness—
The lack of polish and address,
    The villainy in short,
Of serving what explorers think
To be a necessary drink
In bottles holding something less
    Than one Imperial quart,
And costing quite a shilling more
Than many grocers charge ashore.

*

At sea the days go slipping past.
Monotonous from first to last—
A trip like any other one
In vessels going south. The sun
    Grew higher and more fiery.
We lay and drank, and swore, and played
At Trick-my-neighbour in the shade;
And you may guess how every sight,
However trivial or slight,
    Was noted in my diary.
I have it here—the usual things—
A serpent (not the sort with wings)
    Came rising from the sea:
In length (as far as we could guess)
A quarter of a mile or less.
The weather was extremely clear,
The creature dangerously near
    And plain as it could be.
It had a bifurcated tail,
And in its mouth it held a whale.
Just north, I find, of Cape de Verd
We caught a very curious bird
    With horns upon its head;
And—not, as one might well suppose,
Web-footed or with jointed toes—
    But having hoofs instead.
As no one present seemed to know
Its use or name, I let it go.

138

On June the 7th after dark
A young and very hungry shark
   Came climbing up the side.
It ate the Chaplain and the Mate—
But why these incidents relate?
   The public must decide,
That nothing in the voyage out
Was worth their bothering about,
Until we saw the coast, which looks
Exactly as it does in books.

V

Oh! Africa, mysterious Land!
Surrounded by a lot of sand
   And full of grass and trees,
And elephants and Afrikanders,
And politics and Salamanders,
And Germans seeking to annoy,
And horrible rhinoceroi,
And native rum in little kegs,
And savages called Touaregs
   (A kind of Soudanese).
And tons of diamonds, and lots
Of nasty, dirty Hottentots,
And coolies coming from the East;
And serpents, seven yards long at least,
   And lions, that retain
Their vigour, appetites and rage
Intact to an extreme old age,
   And never lose their mane.
Far Land of Ophir! Mined for gold
By lordly Solomon of old,
Who sailing northward to Perim
Took all the gold away with him,
   And left a lot of holes;
Vacuities that bring despair
   To those confiding souls

Who find that they have bought a share
In marvellous horizons, where
The Desert terrible and bare
   Interminably rolls.

Great Island! Made to be the bane
Of Mr Joseph Chamberlain.
Peninsula! Whose smouldering fights
Keep Salisbury awake at nights;
And furnished for a year or so
Such sport to M. Hanotaux.

Vast Continent! Whose cumbrous shape
Runs from Bizerta to the Cape
(Bizerta on the northern shore,
Concerning which, the French, they swore
It never should be fortified,
Wherein that cheerful people lied).

Thou nest of Sultans full of guile,
Embracing Zanzibar the vile
And Egypt, watered by the Nile
(Egypt, which is, as I believe,
The property of the Khedive):
Containing in thy many states
Two independent potentates,
   And one I may not name.
(Look carefully at number three,
Not independent quite, but he
Is more than what he used to be.)
To thee, dear goal, so long deferred
Like old Aeneas—in a word
   To Africa we came.

We beached upon a rising tide
At Sasstown on the western side;
   And as we touched the strand
I thought (I may have been mistook)

I thought the earth in terror shook
    To feel its Conquerors land.

V I

In getting up our Caravan
We met a most obliging man,
The Lord Chief Justice of Liberia,
And Minister of the Interior;
Cain Abolition Beecher Boz,
Worked like a Nigger—which he was—
    And in a single day
Procured us Porters, Guides, and kit,
And would not take a sou for it
    Until we went away.*
We wondered how this fellow made
Himself so readily obeyed,
And why the natives were so meek;
Until by chance we heard him speak,
And then we clearly understood
How great a Power for Social Good
    The African can be.
He said with a determined air:
'You are not what your fathers were;
Liberians, you are Free!
Of course, if you refuse to go——'
And here he made a gesture.
He also gave us good advice
Concerning Labour and its Price.
'In dealing wid de Native Scum,
Yo' cannot pick an' choose;
Yo' hab to promise um a sum
Ob wages, paid in Cloth and Rum.
But, Lordy! that's a ruse!
Yo' get yo' well on de Adventure,
And change de wages to Indenture.'

---

* But when we went away, we found
    A deficit of several pound.

141

We did the thing that he projected,
The Caravan grew disaffected,
    And Sin and I consulted;
Blood understood the Native mind.
He said: 'We must be firm but kind.'
    A Mutiny resulted.
I never shall forget the way
That Blood upon this awful day
Preserved us all from death.
He stood upon a little mound,
Cast his lethargic eyes around,
And said beneath his breath:
'Whatever happens we have got
The Maxim Gun, and they have not.'

He marked them in their rude advance,
He hushed their rebel cheers;
With one extremely vulgar glance
He broke the Mutineers.
(I have a picture in my book
Of how he quelled them with a look.)
We shot and hanged a few, and then
The rest became devoted men.
And here I wish to say a word
Upon the way my heart was stirred
    By those pathetic faces.
Surely our simple duty here
Is both imperative and clear;
While they support us, we should lend
Our every effort to defend,
And from a higher point of view
To give the full direction due
    To all the native races.
And I, throughout the expedition,
Insisted upon this position.

VII

Well, after that we toiled away
At drawing maps, and day by day
Blood made an accurate survey
   Of all that seemed to lend
A chance, no matter how remote,
Of letting our financier float
That triumph of Imagination,
'The Libyan Association'.
   In this the 'Negroes' friend'
Was much concerned to show the way
Of making Missionaries pay.

At night our leader and our friend
   Would deal in long discourses
Upon this meritorious end,
And how he would arrange it.
'The present way is an abuse
   Of Economic Forces;
They Preach, but they do not Produce.
Observe how I would change it.
I'd have the Missionary lent,
Upon a plot of land,
A sum at twenty-five per cent;
And (if I understand
The kind of people I should get)
An ever-present fear of debt
Would make them work like horses,
And form the spur, or motive spring,
In what I call "developing
   The Natural resources";
While people who subscribe will find
Profit and Piety combined.'

Imagine how the Mighty Scheme,
The Goal, the Vision, and the Dream
Developed in his hands!

With such a purpose, such a mind
Could easily become inclined
To use the worst of lands!
Thus once we found him standing still,
Enraptured, on a rocky hill;
Beneath his feet there stank
A swamp immeasurably wide,
Wherein a kind of foetid tide
Rose rhythmical and sank,
Brackish and pestilent with weeds
And absolutely useless reeds,
It lay; but nothing daunted
At seeing how it heaved and steamed
He stood triumphant, and he seemed
Like one possessed or haunted.

With arms that welcome and rejoice,
We heard him gasping, in a voice
By strong emotion rendered harsh:
'That Marsh—that Admirable Marsh!'
The Tears of Avarice that rise
In purely visionary eyes,
Were rolling down his nose.
He was no longer Blood the Bold,
The Terror of his foes;
But Blood inflamed with greed of gold.

He saw us, and at once became
The Blood we knew, the very same
Whom we had loved so long.
He looked affectionately sly,
And said, 'Perhaps you wonder why
My feelings are so strong?
You only see a swamp, but I——
My friends, I will explain it.
I know some gentlemen in town
Will give me fifty thousand down,
Merely for leave to drain it.'

A little later on we found
A piece of gently rolling ground
That showed above the flat.
Such a protuberance or rise
As wearies European eyes.
To common men, like Sin and me
The Eminence appeared to be
As purposeless as that.
Blood saw another meaning there,
He turned with a portentous glare,
And shouted for the Native Name.
The Black interpreter in shame
Replied: 'The native name I fear
Is something signifying Mud.'
    Then, with the gay bravado
That suits your jolly Pioneer,
In his prospectus Captain Blood
    Baptised it 'Eldorado'.
He also said the Summit rose
Majestic with Eternal Snows.

VIII

Now it behoves me (or behooves)
To give a retrospect that proves
    What foresight can achieve,
The kind of thing that (by the way)
Men in our cold agnostic day
Must come from Africa to say,
    From England to believe.

Blood had, while yet we were in town,
Said with his intellectual frown:
'Suppose a Rhino knocks you down
And walks upon you like a mat,
Think of the public irritation.
If with an incident like that,
We cannot give an illustration.'

145

Seeing we should be at a loss
To reproduce the scene,
We bought a stuffed rhinoceros,
A Kodak, and a screen.
We fixed a picture. William pressed
A button, and I did the rest.

To those Carnivora that make
An ordinary Person quake
    We did not give a care.
The Lion never will attack
A White, if he can get a Black.
And there were such a lot of these
We could afford with perfect ease
    To spare one here and there.
It made us more compact—and then—
It's right to spare one's fellow men.

Of far more consequence to us,
And much more worthy to detain us,
    The very creature that we feared
(I mean the white Rhinoceros,
'Siste Viator Africanus')
    In all its majesty appeared.

This large, but peevish pachyderm
(To use a scientific term),
Though commonly herbivorous,
Is eminently dangerous.
It may be just the creature's play;
But people who have felt it say
That when he prods you with his horn
You wish you never had been born.

As I was dozing in the sun,
Without a cartridge to my gun,
    Upon a sultry day,
Absorbed in somnolescent bliss,

Just such an animal as this
    Came charging where I lay.
My only refuge was to fly,
But flight is not for me!*
Blood happened to be standing by,
He darted up a tree
And shouted, 'Do your best to try
And fix him with the Human Eye.'

Between a person and a beast
(But for the Human Eye at least)
The issue must be clear.
The tension of my nerves increased,
And yet I felt no fear.
Nay, do not praise me—not at all—
Courage is merely physical,
And several people I could name
Would probably have done the same.

I kept my glance extremely firm,
I saw the wretched creature squirm;
A look of terror overspread
Its features, and it dropped down dead.
At least, I thought it did,
And foolishly withdrew my gaze,
When (finding it was rid
Of those mysterious piercing rays)
    It came to life again.
It jumped into the air, and came
With all its might upon my frame.

(Observe the posture of the hoof.
The wire and black support that look
So artificial in the proof
Will be deleted in the book.)

* Besides, I found my foot was caught
  In twisted roots that held it taut.

147

It did it thirty separate times;
When, luckily for all these rhymes,
Blood shot the brute—that is to say,
Blood shot, and then it ran away.

IX

We journeyed on in single file;
The march proceeded mile on mile
    Monotonous and lonely,
We saw (if I remember right)
The friendly features of a white
    On two occasions only.
The first was when our expedition
Came suddenly on a commission,
    Appointed to determine
Whether the thirteenth parallel
Ran right across a certain well,
Or touched a closely neighbouring tree;
And whether elephants should be
Exterminated all as 'game',
Or, what is not at all the same,
    Destroyed as common vermin.

To this commission had been sent
Great bigwigs from the Continent,
    And on the English side
Men of such ancient pedigree
As filled the soul of Blood with glee;
    He started up and cried:
'I'll go to them at once, and make
These young adventurous spirits take
    A proof of my desire
To use in this concern of ours
Their unsuspected business powers.
The bearers of historic names
    Shall rise to something higher
Than haggling over frontier claims,

And they shall find their last estate
Enshrined in my directorate.'

In twenty minutes he returned,
His face with righteous anger burned,
    And when we asked him what he'd done,
He answered, 'They reject us,
I couldn't get a single one
    To come on the prospectus.
Their leader (though he was a Lord)
Stoutly refused to join the board,
And made a silly foreign speech
Which sounded like No Bless Ableech.
I'm used to many kinds of men,
And bore it very well; but, when
    It came to being twitted
On my historic Sporting Shirt,
I own I felt a trifle hurt;
    I took my leave and quitted.'

There is another side to this;
With no desire to prejudice
    The version of our leader,
I think I ought to drop a hint
Of what I shall be bound to print,
    In justice to the reader.
I followed, keeping out of sight;
And took in this ingenious way
A sketch that throws a certain light
On *why* the master went away.
No doubt he felt a trifle hurt,
It even may be true to say
They twitted him upon his shirt.
But isn't it a trifle thick
To talk of twitting with a stick?
Well, let it pass. He acted well.
This species of official swell,

Especially the peer,
Who stoops to a delimitation
With any European nation
    Is doomed to disappear.
Blood said, 'They pass into the night.'
And men like Blood are always right.

The Second shows the full effect
Of ministerial neglect;
Sin, walking out alone in quest
Of Boa-constrictors that infest
    The Lagos Hinterland,
Got separated from the rest,
    And ran against a band
Of native soldiers led by three—
A Frenchman, an official Prussian,
And what we took to be a Russian—
    The very coalition
Who threaten England's power at sea,
And, but for men like Blood and me,
Would drive her navies from the sea,
    And hurl her to perdition.
But did my comrade think to flee?
To use his very words—Not he!
He turned with a contemptuous laugh.
Observe him in the photograph.
But still these bureaucrats pursued,
Until they reached the Captain's tent.
They grew astonishingly rude;
The Russian simply insolent,
Announcing that he had been sent
    Upon a holy mission,
To call for the disarmament
    Of all our expedition.
He said 'the miseries of war
Had touched his master to the core';
    It was extremely vexing
To hear him add, 'he couldn't stand

This passion for absorbing land;
    He hoped we weren't annexing.'
The German asked with some brutality
To have our names and nationality.
    I had an inspiration,
In words methodical and slow
I gave him this decisive blow:
    'I haven't got a nation.'
Perhaps the dodge was rather low,
And yet I wasn't wrong to
Escape the consequences so;
For, on my soul, I did not know
What nation to belong to.

The German gave a searching look,
And marked me in his little book:
'The features are a trifle Dutch—
    Perhaps he is a Fenian;
He may be a Maltese, but much
    More probably Armenian.'

Blood gave us each a trifling sum
To say that he was deaf and dumb,
    And backed the affirmation
By gestures so extremely rum,
They marked him on the writing pad;
'Not only deaf and dumb, but mad.'
    It saved the situation.
'If such a man as *that*' (said they)
'Is Leader, they can go their way.'

X

Thus, greatly to our ease of mind,
Our foreign foes we left behind;
But dangers even greater
Were menacing our path instead.
In every book I ever read
Of travels on the Equator,

A plague, mysterious and dread,
Imperils the narrator;
He always very nearly dies,
But doesn't, which is calm and wise.
Said Sin, the indolent and vague,
'D' you think that we shall get the plague?'
It followed tragically soon;
In fording an immense lagoon,
We let our feet get damp.
Next morning I began to sneeze,
The awful enemy, Disease,
Had fallen on the camp!
With Blood the malady would take
An allotropic form
Of intermittent stomach ache,
While Sin grew over warm;
Complained of weakness in the knees,
An inability to think,
A strong desire to dose and drink,
    And lie upon his back.
For many a long delirious day,
Each in his individual way,
    Succumbed to the attack.

XI

Our litters lay upon the ground
With heavy curtains shaded round;
    The Plague had passed away.
We could not hear a single sound,
    And wondered as we lay—
'Perhaps the Forest Belt is passed,
And Timbuctoo is reached at last,
The while our faithful porters keep
So still to let their masters sleep.'

Poor Blood and I were far too weak
To raise ourselves, or even speak;

We lay, content to languish.
When Sin, to make the matter certain,
Put out his head beyond the curtain.
   And cried in utter anguish:
'This is not Timbuctoo at all,
But just a native Kraal or Crawl;
And, what is more, our Caravan
Has all deserted to a man.'

*

At evening they returned to bring
Us prisoners to their savage king,
   Who seemed upon the whole
A man urbane and well inclined;
He said, 'You shall not be confined,
   But left upon parole.'
Blood, when he found us both alone,
Lectured in a pedantic tone,
   And yet with quaint perfection,
On 'Prison Systems I have known'.
   He said in this connection:

'The primal process is to lug
A Johnny to the cells—or jug.
Dear Henry will not think me rude,
If—just in passing—I allude
To Quod or Penal Servitude.
Of every form, Parole I take
To be the easiest to break.'

On hearing this we ran
To get the guns, and then we laid
An admirable ambuscade,
In which to catch our man.
We hid behind a little knoll,
   And waited for our prey
To take his usual morning stroll
   Along the fatal way.

All unsuspecting and alone
He came into the danger zone,
    The range of which we knew
To be one furlong and a third,
And then—an incident occurred
Which, I will pledge my sacred word,
    Is absolutely true.

Blood took a very careful aim,
And Sin and I did just the same;
Yet by some strange and potent charm
The King received no kind of harm!
    He wore, as it appears,
A little fetish on a thread,
A mumbo-jumbo, painted red,
Gross and repulsive in the head,
    Especially the ears.

Last year I should have laughed at it,
But now with reverence I admit
That nothing in the world is commoner
Than Andrew Lang's Occult Phenomena.

On getting back to England, I
Described the matter to the Psy-
    Chological Committee.

Of course they thanked me very much;
But said, 'We have a thousand such,
    And it would be a pity
To break our standing resolution,
And pay for any contribution.'

XII

The King was terribly put out;
To hear him call the guard and shout,
    And stamp, and curse, and rave
Was (as the Missionaries say)

A lesson in the Godless way
The heathen will behave.
He sent us to a prison, made
Of pointed stakes in palisade,
    And there for several hours
Our Leader was a mark for bricks,
And eggs and coconuts and sticks,
    And pussy-cats in showers.
Our former porters seemed to bear
A grudge against the millionaire.

And yet the thing I minded most
    Was not the ceaseless teasing
(With which the Captain was engrossed),
Nor being fastened to a post
(Though that was far from pleasing);
But hearing them remark that they
'Looked forward to the following day'.

XIII

At length, when we were left alone,
Sin twisted with a hollow groan,
    And bade the Master save
His comrades by some bold device,
    From the impending grave.

Said Blood: 'I never take advice,
But every man has got his price;
We must maintain the open door
Yes, even at the cost of war!'
    He shifted his position,
And drafted in a little while
A note in diplomatic style
    Containing a condition.

'If them that wishes to be told
As how there is a bag of gold,
    And where a party hid it;

Mayhap as other parties knows
A thing or two, and there be those
      As seen the man wot hid it.'
The Monarch read it through, and wrote
A little sentence most emphatical:
'I think the language of the note
Is strictly speaking not grammatical.'
On seeing our acute distress,
The King—I really must confess—
      Behaved uncommon handsome;
He said he would release the three
If only Captain Blood and he
      Could settle on a ransom.
And it would clear the situation
To hear his private valuation.

'My value,' William Blood began,
'Is ludicrously small.
I think I am the vilest man
That treads this earthly ball;
My head is weak, my heart is cold,
I'm ugly, vicious, vulgar, old,
Unhealthy, short and fat.
I cannot speak, I cannot work,
I have the temper of a Turk,
      And cowardly at that.
Retaining, with your kind permission,
The usual five per cent commission,
I think that I could do the job
For seventeen or sixteen bob.'

The King was irritated, frowned,
And cut him short with, 'Goodness Gracious!
Your economics *are* fallacious!
I quite believe you are a wretch,
But things are worth what they will fetch.
I'll put your price at something round,
Say, six-and-thirty thousand pound?'

But just as Blood began with zest,
To bargain, argue, and protest,
    Commander Sin and I
Broke in: 'Your Majesty was told
About a certain bag of gold;
    If you will let us try,
We'll find the treasure, for we know
The place to half a yard or so.'

Poor William! The suspense and pain
Had touched the fibre of his brain;
    So far from showing gratitude,
He cried in his delirium: 'Oh!
For Heaven's sake don't let them go.'
        Only a lunatic would take
            So singular an attitude,
        When loyal comrades for his sake
        Had put their very lives at stake.
                        *
The King was perfectly content
To let us find it—and we went.
But as we left we heard him say,
    'If there is half an hour's delay
        The Captain will have passed away.'

                    XIV

Alas! within a single week
The Messengers despatched to seek
    Our hiding-place had found us,
We made an excellent defence
(I use the word in legal sense),
    But none the less they bound us.
    (Not in the legal sense at all
But with a heavy chain and ball)
With barbarism past belief
They flaunted in our faces
The relics of our noble chief;

With insolent grimaces,
Raised the historic shirt before
Our eyes, and pointed on the floor
To dog-eared cards and loaded dice;
It seems they sold him by the slice.
Well, every man has got his price.

The horrors followed thick and fast,
I turned my head to give a last
Farewell to Sin; but, ah! too late,
I only saw his horrid fate—
Some savages around a pot
That seemed uncomfortably hot;
And in the centre of the group
My dear companion making soup.

Then I was pleased to recognise
Two thumbscrews suited to my size,
And I was very glad to see
That they were going to torture me.
I find that torture pays me best,
It simply teems with interest.

They hung me up above the floor
Head downwards by a rope;
They thrashed me half an hour or more,
They filled my mouth with soap;
They jabbed me with a pointed pole
To make me lose my self-control,
     But they did not succeed.
Till (if it's not too coarse to state)
There happened what I simply hate,
     My nose began to bleed.
Then, I admit, I said a word
Which luckily they never heard;
But in a very little while
My calm and my contemptuous smile

Compelled them to proceed.
They filed my canine teeth to points
   And made me bite my tongue.
They racked me till they burst my joints,
   And after that they hung
A stone upon my neck that weighed
At least a hundred pounds, and made
Me run like mad for twenty miles,
And climb a lot of lofty stiles.
They tried a dodge that rarely fails,
The tub of Regulus with nails—
The cask is rather rude and flat,
But native casks are all like that—
The nails stuck in for quite an inch,
But did I flinch? I did not flinch.
In tones determined, loud, and strong
I sang a patriotic song,
Thank Heaven it did not last for long!
   My misery was past;
My superhuman courage rose
Superior to my savage foes;
   They worshipped me at last.
With many heartfelt compliments,
They sent me back at their expense,
And here I am returned to find
The pleasures I had left behind.

To go the London rounds!
To note the quite peculiar air
Of courtesy, and everywhere
The same unfailing public trust
In manuscript that fetches just
A thousand! not of thin Rupees,
Nor Reis (which are Portuguese),
Nor Rubles; but a thousand clear
Of heavy, round, impressive, dear,
Familiar English pounds!

Oh! England, who would leave thy shores—
Excuse me, but I see it bores
A busy journalist
To hear a rhapsody which he
Could write without detaining me,
So I will not insist.
Only permit me once again
    To make it clearly understood
That both those honourable men,
    Commander Sin and Captain Blood,
Would swear to all that I have said,
Were they alive;
    but they are dead!